THE COLLECTED WORKS OF BUCK ROGERS IN THE 25th CENTURY

THE COLLECTED WORKS OF BUCK ROGERS IN THE 25th CENTURY

INTRODUCTION BY RAY BRADBURY

EDITOR/ROBERT C. DILLE

CHELSEA HOUSE PUBLISHERS

PREFACE

This book records the unique story of how a comic strip became an inspiration to youth. For the most part, its message told youth of all ages that the opportunities of the future are boundless, that science beats superstition, and that education can make all things possible.

On January 7, 1929, the Buck Rogers comic strip made its first newspaper appearance. Philip Nowlan created the story, basing it upon his articles "Armageddon, 2419 A.D." and "The Airlords of Han," which *Amazing Stories* magazine had published in August, 1928, and March, 1929. The idea for the futuristic comic strip, however, originated with John Flint Dille, the President of the National Newspaper Syndicate of America who convinced a somewhat reluctant Nowlan to undertake the strip. As an inducement to Nowlan, who doubted his ability with the comic strip medium, Dille suggested that Nowlan take the first episode from "Armageddon, 2419 A.D." and change the hero's name from Anthony Rogers to Buck Rogers. Dille then enlisted Dick Calkins, an editorial cartoonist, to illustrate the story.

In submitting his first copy to Dille on September 13, 1928, Nowlan, anticipating national syndication, noted:

"I've dragged in the names of several cities and worked a few more into the script. You will be explaining to the papers, I imagine, that sooner or later we are going to get their cities into it. It's only natural that Buck should be sent on many important missions to the different sections of the country. As a matter of fact, sooner or later he will have to duck across the ocean to see how the European races are making out and arrange a hasty treaty or two with the fighting Irish, the sturdy Germans, the Independent Italians, the noble Poles and Checko-Slovakinans [sic] and so on."

But by the time the strip ended in 1967 Buck had traveled to the Moon, Mars, Venus, and numerous other celestial bodies.

In the first episode Buck Rogers met Wilma Deering, a symbol of oppressed 25th-century Americans. The United States had fallen under the domination of an Asiatic race which controlled the rocket ships and disintegrater rays which the Americans had to recapture before they could liberate themselves. Gradually, time flying belts, rocket ships, rocket pistols, gravity repeller rays, disintegrater beams, futuristic cities, and electronic truth machines were brought into the story, diagrammed and explained in intricate detail.

Reader interest was stimulated by references to American cities—a device which also served to sell the strip to local editors. Pittsburgh editors were lured by "Alleghany Orgzone." Niagra became the capital of Earth, inducement enough for the editor of the Buffalo *Evening News*. Also mentioned by name in the first episodes were San Francisco, Detroit, and New York. Within a few months, however, as the strip prospered, Buck became an explorer of the universe. Between 1929 and 1967, Buck Rogers had been translated into eighteen languages and had appeared in more than 450 newspapers.

In preparing this book, I have incurred many agreeable debts of gratitude. Eugene R. Seger of Detroit, Michigan, Ed Aprill of Ann Arbor, Michigan, Tony Goodstone of New York City and my brother John Flint Dille, Jr. of Elkhart, Indiana made numerous suggestions and generously shared with me their knowledge of Buck Rogers.

I do not dedicate this collection. It was dedicated to youth by the three inspired men who put the story across—Phil Nowlan, Dick Calkins and John Flint Dille. No less a dedication to youth was made by the successors to this departed trio. They are too numerous to mention, beyond Rick Yager, who began as a schoolboy—apprentice to Dick Calkins in 1932, and who carried on with Buck Rogers for a quarter of a century.

Robert C. Dille

Chicago
October 25, 1969

CONTENTS

BUCK ROGERS IN APOLLO YEAR 1

The most beautiful sound in my life, dearly recollected, fully remembered, was the sound of a folded newspaper kiteing through the summer air and landing on my front porch.

Every late afternoon from the time I was nine until I was fourteen that sound, and the thump it made hitting the side of the house, or the screen-door, or a window, but never the porch-planks themselves, that sound had an immediate effect upon one person inside the house.

The door burst wide. A boy, myself, leapt out, eyes blazing, mouth gasping for breath, hands seizing at the paper to grapple it wide so that the hungry soul of one of Waukegan, Illinois' finest small intellects could feed upon:

BUCK ROGERS IN THE 25TH CENTURY.

That is how I lived—in a fever, a faint delerium, in semi-hysteria. I was born and bred fanatic. When I loved, I truly loved. When I went mad, I was Ahab's cabin boy, madness maddened.

In fact, I still live pretty much that way. That boy still uses my soul as a trampoline. And Buck Rogers was his first, *my* first, huge mania. You note I speak as if there were two of us. But isn't that true for all of us? Is there not the soul that celebrates and the more practical body that watches from the grandstand, admiring, applauding, as the parade-of-one goes by? How does one come by such manias? How do you explain such feelings to others? I have no easy answers. In any event, I *was*.

And what I was began, as it did for millions of other boys in the early Twenties, with motion-pictures. THE HUNCHBACK OF NOTRE DAME with Lon Chaney, MR. WU, LONDON AFTER MIDNIGHT, and THE PHANTOM OF THE OPERA grew me; THE CAT AND THE CANARY, THE BAT, and THE GORILLA shaped me. So, by the time I was nine, on the verge of collision with Buck Rogers, I was a real child of the 20th Century. Which means, long before McLuhan, I was a visual person. And I fed my eyes not only on films but picture books and the treasures of the Chicago museums. I fell prey to an early and immense love for Tyrannosaurus Rex, Brontosaurus, Pterodactyl.

From the immense dead creatures of the past it was a natural step, for me anyway, to the immense pretending-to-be-alive machines of the future. It was in 1928 that I made the shift from a life of pure film-going and dared to infuse myself with the first science-fiction magazines, which most gratifyingly combined Pterodactyl with far-traveling rocket. The "long-since-dust joined with the not-yet-arrived" remained a constant companion in all the years when I just never grew up.

Get on it with it, you say. For God's sake, stop snittering, and deliver Buck Rogers.

But, you see, I can't do that just yet. For Buck Rogers is meaningless unless I can somehow isolate you from your material goodies for awhile—your car, your house, your accumulation of tape recorders, radios, tvs, etc, etc, and plump you down in 1929, and by some miracle turn you into a child of nine. What was the world like then? It was a world without even so much as one small rocket, or the promise of one. Oh, yes, later on we were to remember there were a few wild men like Professor Goddard stirring about. But no one gave him mind. He was a blathering idiot, a fool, a nothing. Von Braun? He was a teenager somewhere in Germany smitten with Fritz Lang's film GIRL IN THE MOON, starting a cuckoo rocket society, standing out under the stars at night, a has-been who would never be. And, in 1929, think of it! Why, good grief, Armstrong, Aldrin, and Collins hadn't even been born yet!

In 1929 you would have found few decent roads and no really good cross-continental highways. We were eighty million people less than we are today. The first streamlined trains were merely in blueprint stage. No one had broken the sound barrier. In fact, it was impossible of breakage, and anyone who dared try his spunk against the gods of aerodynamics would be shattered like so much porcelain. That much was fact. That much was truly known.

Passenger air service across the country? A few thousand people had the money. The other 120 million took the train, departed the color of milk, arrived the color of soot.

If you had had a million dollars in those days you couldn't have bought, much less found, a tape recorder. Television? We would invent that in the year 1999, maybe. Radio? The merest

infant, born only a few years before. Films, also, had begun to speak up, use sound, a scant few months before Dick Calkins sat down to draw Buck Rogers.

So, for all intents and purposes, compared to 1969, I was raised, all of the Twenties boys were raised, in the last steams of Steamboat America, in the last go-round of the fringed surreys, milk-trucks, and ice-wagons drawn by summer-lazy horses.

To beat my point to the finest frazzle, try to recall the comic strip CAP STUBBS—that was me and my grandma. The whole family in the daily cartoon OUT OUT WAY was my family, teetering on the gnawed edge of middle class, dumb to the fact that new mechanical beasts would soon push us all over hell. No wonder then that Buck Rogers burst upon our vision like some grander July Fourth, full of rockets celebrating tomorrow.

And when Buck did arrive, how much better than the parlor's throat-clearing Victrola, which my Uncle Bion had just rebuilt into a ten-dialed radio filled with nine thousand tubes which brought in a ton of static from *alpha centauri* and a chamber quartet playing music-to-sleep-by in Schenectady. How grand Buck's world was compared to the empty garage at our house, or the one next door with the 1924 Kissel Kar stashed therein.

And what did Buck Rogers write on the sky of northern Illinois? What did Phil Nowlan and Dick Calkins have so urgently to say to those of us who stomached down on the afternoon papers to fall in love with Other Times?

They said: why wait? The time is now. Run, boy, run. Inhabit these ideas, speak these baloons, *be* the future. And, with a cat's-hair crystal radio in one pocket and our Lon Chaney vampire-teeth in the other, beaten down by dull reality, dying for romance, we waded out into the sea of space and happily drowned.

What, specifically, did Buck Rogers have to offer that instantly ''zapped'' us into blind gibbers of love? Well, to start out with mere trifles, in strip number 1 (as you will see here): rocket guns that shoot explosive bullets; people who fly through the air with ''jumping belts'' (later to become rocket-belts which lifted people by jet propellants, which, of course, everyone *knew* would never be invented); ''hovercrafts'' skimming over the surface of the earth; disintegrators which destroyed, down to the meanest atom, anything they touched; radar-equipped robot armies; television-controlled rockets and rocket bombs; invasions from Mars, the first landing on the Moon—

Hold on. Think of that for a moment. In 1929 our thinking was so primitive we could scarcely imagine the years before a machine capable of footprinting moon dust would be invented. And even that prediction was snorted at, declared impossible by 99 per cent of the people. And Buck Rogers offered us more: a trip to the asteroids, a journey to Venus, Mercury, and, yes, Jupiter itself.

Regarding the various styles with which Buck Rogers was drawn, even now it is impossible for me to judge the artistic value of the panels without the old passions and rumors of passions of my childhood rising up.

I am inclined to believe it was not so much how the episodes were drawn but what was *happening* in them that made the strip such a success. The enemy of every boy is gravity, and here in the first few days of Buck Rogers that incredible stuff ''inertron'' plucks us off our feet and hurls us through the sky, free at last. And free not only to jump over dogs, rivers, and skyscrapers, but to challenge the stars.

Yes, earlier in the 20th century other cartoonists had shown the interplanetary wanderings of such characters as Little Nemo. But all that was fantasy. Buck Rogers, now, was the coming reality, fantasy with a vengeance, dreams suddenly peeling off the bedroom wall into three dimensions that moved, re-created themselves, and became yet further dreams.

All this being true, who shall we credit with the genesis of Buck Rogers? The names of Phil Nowlan, writer, and Dick Calkins, illustrator, are well known to all of us. But the man who had the large vision to begin with was John F. Dille, whose newspaper syndicate distributed the comic strip once it was created.

Late in 1926 Dille began to look about at the strange new world that was coming to some sort of shambling puberty insofar as machines were concerned and decided that comic strips were not fulfilling one part of their large potential. He had the idea that comics, day in and day out, could not only entertain but inspire and educate, speak not only in tongues of past and present but in that vast wave of the future he saw rushing in on the shore.

One half of his problem was solved almost immediately. On the staff of his National Newspaper Service was a creative young artist named Dick Calkins. The only problem with Calkins was that he was determined to create a prehistoric strip with cavemen, dinosaurs, sabertooth tigers, and the lot. Dille's job was to completely reverse Calkin's thinking and thereby toss him into the 25th century.

The final problem was finding the correct writer to handle thousands of days of plots and counter-plots.

Fortunately Dille had happened upon a short story, "Armegeddon 2419," by Philip Francis Nowlan which appeared in the August 1928 issue of *Amazing Stories.* But Mr. Nowlan, when approached, was not at all sure of his story's potential as a comic strip. Dille had to convince him that the gamble was worth making. Nowlan finally gambled. Calkins drew. The rest is history.

And, you may well have asked by now, why have I bothered to acknowledge, record, and honor this history? Isn't this all rather trivial? With more important things to do, why would anyone recount the genesis of a comic strip?

And here is where all the pontiff intellectuals, or pseudo-intellectuals if you wish, and Ray Bradbury lock horns. For the one thing that continually amazes me in my fellow human beings, intellectual or not, is their lack of imagination. Having lifted myself, every day of my life, by my mad if not insane bootstraps, it was years before I really glanced about and saw that not only did others lack self-starters, but did not even know their own condition. They imagined themselves clothed; I say them naked. I soon saw, also, that the simplest addition escaped them. And by simple addition I mean man-plus-rocket-equals-Moon. Only in the last few years has that seemed an agreeable arithmetic to millions of souls, regardless of brain sufficiency.

To carry the point further, I have found again and again that the finest minds, the finest colleges, the nicest people, do not know the first thing about Creativity, large C or small, or how to stimulate the darling seed, the eminent root, or the final flower. In fact I have watched supposedly intelligent men hurl themselves with cruel vigor into attacking and destroying the simple root systems of creativity. Nothing mediocre must be considered. Dandelions must be destroyed for the rose. And the thing these men fear, in simple or compound forms, is imagination. And the outcrop of imagination we call romance. Or any combination of these which are summoned out of our intuition.

But we have fallen on bad times. Which means we are data-oriented. If the data doesn't all fall into neat rows and add up to preconceived sums, we must reject it. True wisdom would tell us otherwise but, fools that we are, we keep on crying out that only Facts are true, only Data counts. No dreams allowed. Not a hair of intuition, please. No romance. No fun.

Well, without romance, without fun, the soul of man turns over, curls up its toes, groans, withers, dies. These bank tellers, these ledger keepers, these snobs somehow influenced me as I grew up. These potato people, with their easy moron-disguised-as-super-bright laughter, convinced me, albeit briefly, when I was ten that I was wrong.

And I gave away my Buck Rogers collection.

My Buck Rogers Collection! Which was like giving away my head, my heart, my soul, and half a lung. I walked wounded for a year after that. I grieved and cursed myself for having so dumbly tossed aside what was, in essence, the greatest love of my life.

Imagination. Romance. Intuition. Love.

I soon saw that everyone else was wrong and that, lonely or not, put upon or not, I was right. The Future was rushing across the sky. Mr. Dille saw it. Mr. Calkins and Mr. Nowlan saw it. I saw it. And there was only one thing to do—start collecting the Buck Rogers daily and Sunday strips all over again. Because, aged ten, I had made the greatest discovery of all, the discovery that every scientist and thinker, every shaker and mover has made: we must be children before we are adults; we must crawl before we walk and walk before we run and run before we take off and . . . FLY; we must be poor before we are mediocre, and lovely-mediocre before we know excellence. And excellence and quality are only reached by snuffing in and knowing to the last molecule all there is to know about bad, not-so-bad, better, best, and so on down the line, cycle after cycle.

You do not start with quality. You start with dreams and the dreams must be large because you are so small, so unequal to the tasks you wish to set for yourself. But you must start somewhere, and somewhere lies between the left ear and the right, and if someone comes

along with enough wit and verve to put it on paper with pen and ink, *that's* the direction, and off you go!

In all the years of all the laughing, the snorting, the doubtful, the derisive people, only a few made sense to me and I must honor them here, for they truly inspired me, filled me with love, and allowed my intuition to come out to play forever in the fields of space.

The history of the world is the history of such cyclings and re-cyclings. Boys need to take courage wherever they can find it. Jules Verne wrote of insubstantial submarines. A twelve year old boy, reading Verne, declared, "I shall grow up and invent the first practical submarine!" He did just that. Admiral Byrd, at the North Pole, said: "Jules Verne leads me." What a triumph of creative, aesthetic, adventurous scientific ventriloquism! The old Frenchman, long since dead, speaks out of the young American's mouth, even as lost strange beauties of voices speak from Edison's first miraculous phonographs.

We live by example. We write to exemplify. When the fires die, we stir up new fires. And the art forms, popular or elevated to rare ivory towers, are those new fires. My God, when are we going to relax and know and accept all this, and get on with our creativity without feeling guilty or having to alibi for great loves which seem silly or trivial to others?

Enough. I have already gone on too long.

All Hail, John Dille, Dick Calkins, and Phil Nowlan.

Here's the collection.

But, as I have indicated, the only way to see its future is by leaping backward. I offer you the services of my own time machine, located back in the soft summer of 1929 before the world fell apart. Not only will my machine travel in time, but, most important, your body and mind and soul will become those of a nine-year-old boy, such creature as was first invented by God in search of a catapult.

There you are, waiting, trembling, in fevers; so full of life that if you were a volcano you'd come up in someone's cornfield and bury the silo. There you are, as afternoon slides toward warm dusk; eyes shut, listening. . . .

And there's the sound, whistling through the air, crashing along the shingles, sliding down the roof, falling to the porch.

You fling the door wide. You bend to touch that incredible newspaper with a hot hand.

BUCK ROGERS has just been born.

And you, a single wise small boy, are there alone to welcome him to a world he will help change forever.

Ray Bradbury

Los Angeles
October 18, 1969

BUCK ROGERS: AN AUTOBIOGRAPHY

I, BUCK ROGERS, am the only man alive, so far as I know, whose normal span of life has been spread over a period of five centuries! I was just twenty years old when the great World War of 1914-18 ended and I was mustered out of the Air Service where I had served for eighteen months on the battle fronts of France as a Pursuit Pilot. Soon after returning home I got a job surveying the low levels of an abandoned mine located near a great city. Deep in this mine, I was cut off from return by a cave-in, and succumbed to a curious and unidentified radio-active gas I had descended to study. I sank into a state of suspended animation in which I was "preserved" in all my youth and vigor until, five hundred years later, some shifting of strata once more let air into the ancient workings—and I awoke.

I had no idea, at first, that I had been unconscious for more than a few hours. But when I staggered up out of the mine a shock awaited me. Gone was every handiwork of man that should have met my eyes, swallowed up in a forest obviously centuries old, though the contours of the valley and the hills opposite were familiar.

I shall pass over the days of mental agony that I spent in the attempt to grasp the meaning of it all, days in which only the necessity of improvising crude traps and clubs with which to secure food preserved me from insanity, and begin with my first glimpse of a Twenty-fifth Century American:

A TWENTY-FIFTH CENTURY AMERICAN

I saw her first through a portion of woodland where the trees were thinly scattered, with dense forest beyond, from which she had just emerged. Overjoyed at the prospect of human companionship at last, I was about to shout, but something in her tense, alert attitude warned me.

She was clad in rather close-fitting garments. Around her waist was a broad belt, and above it, across her shoulders, a sort of pack, of about the proportions of a knapsack. She wore gauntlet gloves and a helmet.

She was backing cautiously away from the denser section of the forest, step by step, when suddenly there came a vivid flash and a detonation like that of a hand grenade some distance to the left of her. She threw up an arm and staggered a bit, in a queer gliding way.

Then recovering, she retreated more rapidly toward me. At every few steps she would raise her arm and, it seemed, merely point here and there into the forest with a curious type of pistol, from the muzzle of which there was no flash nor detonation. But wherever she pointed there was a terrific explosion deep among the trees.

After firing several times she turned quickly toward me, and leaped desperately, and to my amazement, literally sailed through the air, between the scattered trees for a distance of fully ninety feet; though at no time during this jump did she rise higher than about twelve feet off the ground.

But as she completed her leap her foot caught on a projecting root and she sprawled gently forward. I say "gently" for she did not crash down as I would have done, but slid in a weightless sort of way, though when she finally collided with the trunk of a great tree, she seemed to have plenty of *horizontal momentum*. For a moment I stood gaping in amazement. Then, seeing that blood oozed from beneath the tight little helmet, I ran to her, and got another shock; for as I exerted myself to lift her I staggered back and nearly fell, quite unprepared for the lightness of her. She weighed only a few pounds, perhaps 4 or 5.

For a moment I busied myself trying to stanch the flow of blood. But her wound was slight and she was more dazed than hurt. Then I thought of her pursuers, who by this time must have come up within shooting distance. I heard no sound, however.

THE PURSUIT

I took the weapon from her grasp and examined it hastily. It was not unlike the automatic to which I was accustomed. With fumbling fingers I reloaded it with fresh ammunition from her belt, for I heard, not far away, the sound of voices, followed almost immediately by a series of

explosions around us.

Crouching behind a tree, I watched, accustoming myself to the balance of the weapon.

Then I saw a movement in the branches of a tree. The face and shoulders of a man emerged. It was an evil face, and it had murder in it.

That decided me. I raised the gun and fired. My aim was bad for there was no kick at all to the weapon, and I struck the trunk of the tree several feet below the girl's pursuer. But it blew him from his perch like a crumpled bit of paper. And he *floated* to the ground like some limp thing lowered gently by an invisible hand. The tree, its trunk blown apart by the explosion, crashed down.

Then I saw another one of them. He was starting one of those amazing leaps from one tree to another, about forty feet away. Again I fired. This time I scored a direct hit, and the fellow completely vanished in the explosion, blown to atoms.

How many more of them were there I don't know, but this must have been too much for them, for shortly afterward I heard them swishing and crashing away through the tree tops.

I now turned my attention to my newly found companion, and observed, as I carried her lightly to the nearby stream, that she was gloriously young and beautiful, and that her apparent lack of weight was due to the lifting power of the strange device strapped across her shoulders; for though slender, she was well developed, and there was firm strength in her lithe young body.

She moaned softly as I gently removed the close fitting little helmet, and there were orange-gold glints of fire in her hair where the little beams of sunlight, filtering through the forest foliage, fell upon it.

Her injury was really trifling, though the blow had stunned her. Still holding her lightly in my arm, I washed away the blood with water from the stream. At the refreshing touch she moved a bit, and half opened her eyes, and looked at me, it seemed, without the full realization of consciousness. Then she sighed and relaxed. "Thanks," she murmured. "That f-feels good. I'll—I'll be all right in a moment." And unconsciously she snuggled a bit closer in my arm.

THE AWAKENING

Then I felt her body stiffen, and she was looking at me with wide, startled blue eyes. For a moment she was as one paralyzed with amazement. Then, in one sudden whirl of violent motion she had torn herself from me and landed some ten feet away facing me in tense, alert hostility. In her hand was the gun, which I had put back in her holster, and there was no doubt about her readiness to squeeze the trigger had I made the least nervous movement.

"Raise your hands!" she commanded in a cold, hard little voice. And I reached for the sky without argument. "You're one of them," she accused. "And I'm taking you in. Where are the others?"

I tried to grin, but fear it was a sickly effort, for the gun in her hand looked businesslike, and the blue of her eyes was as cold as ice now. "You mean the man who—who attacked you?" I asked. "No, I'm not one of them. In fact I think I disposed of a couple of them for you—with your gun, which you see I gave back to you."

At this she seemed less sure of herself; but no less suspicious. "Put down your hands if you want to," she conceded. "But at the first break . . ." There was a wealth of meaning in the unfinished sentence.

"Now then," she said, advancing a step, "Who are you? What are you doing here?"

"My name is Buck Rogers," I replied. "And I'm not doing anything much except trying to keep alive with the little game I can catch around here."

"Your clothing is strange," she mused, looking me over from head to foot. "There's something queer about all this. There lies that outlaw over there. You must have captured him, because I didn't. All I remember is making a bip leap, catching my foot in something, and then—I saw stars!"

I explained exactly what happened while she gazed straight into my eyes, her glance never wavering.

"I believe, you," she said finally, and after a moment's hesitation, put away her gun. She took a single easy "step," covering the entire distance between us, and said simply; "Thanks for saving my life. Now what's the rest of the story?"

There was no way out of it. I couldn't invent a yarn successfully to fit conditions in a day and age of which I knew nothing, and I certainly did not expect the girl to believe that I was centuries older than she. But I had to take a chance.

She listened patiently-scornfully incredulous at first, but with more tolerance and growing amazement as I went on. And when I had finished she looked thoughtfully at me for some time.

WILMA

"That's all very hard to believe," she said at length, "but I do believe you, Buck Rogers." She held out her hand. "I am Wilma Deering, of the East Central Org, and I'm just finishing my turn at air patrol."

"Air patrol?" I queried. "But you have no plane here, have you? I don't see how you could use one in this forest."

For a moment she looked puzzled, then laughed. "A plane? Oh yes. Wasn't that what they used to call the old-fashioned airships centuries ago?

"No, I haven't one here, but we have aircraft of many types and all are greatly superior to those in use in the ancient civilization you knew. You don't need them when you have a jumping belt"; she indicated the pack across her shoulders; "unless you're going a long distance. What I mean is, I'm on patrol or guard duty to give warning — with rockets — in case any raiding aircraft of the Red Mongols come this way. But come Buck," she added in a most friendly manner. "We must return at once to the city. And I promise you some amazing sights if the knowledge we have of life as it was lived here five hundreds years ago — back in the 1930's — is true. Great scientific marvels have been brought about since then."

Quickly we stripped the jumping belt from the fallen outlaw. Adjusting it properly on my shoulders, Wilma showed me how to leap with it. My efforts were crude but soon I caught the knack of it, and, although I could not match Wilma for speed or distance, we made rapid progress and at last came in sight of a city so amazing in its magnitude and seeming complexity that my astonishment was boundless.

CONQUEST OF GRAVITY

I found myself in a world in which gravity had been conquered by means of truly marvellous inventions. Science had accomplished wonders.

The mysteries of the jumping belt were explained. It was made of *inertron,* a synthetic element of great *reverse weight* which falls *away* from the center of the Earth instead of *toward* it, and which counterbalances all but a few pounds of the wearer's weight. I learned to leap great heights and distances with that pleasant and effortless ease that made aircraft and other vehicles in the 25th Century unnecessary, and indeed undesirable, for personal transportation, except where speed or protection from the weather was required, or where crowded conditions precluded the use of the jumping belt.

It was a strange sensation at first, to give a little hop that normally would carry me twleve inches off the ground, and shoot into the air some twenty or thirty feet, to drift down and land again almost as lightly as a feather. Or to give a great shove against the ground, and soar sixty or seventy feet upward.

But for *speed leaping* I found it was necessary to cultivate a certain delicate instinct of balance. I felt very much as I had when, as a boy, I ran alongside a horse, letting the animal pull me as I took great, leaping steps. In short, I found that although weight apparently had vanished, *momentum remained* and if I hit anything while shooting forward horizontally, I hit it hard.

It was for this reason that the use of jumping belts in cities, useful as they might have been in leaping to the upper stories of buildings or the upper levels of the vast moving sidewalks, was generally prohibited. The temptation to make speed with them was too great. Too many serious accidents had been caused by those who leaped into crowded places with uncontrollable momentum. But to soar across the country, in great easy leaps of sixty to ninety feet or more at the speed of an ice-skater, was delightful.

WOMEN SOLDIERS

It was, perhaps, all the more delightful to me because my instructor in the art of leaping

was *Wilma Deering,* that slender, blue-eyed golden-haired, high-spirited young *soldier-girl* who was destined to be my companion and capable assistant in so many astounding adventures in this marvelous universe.

Equality of the sexes had been one of the developments brought about during five centuries. It was part of the education of all young girls to spend a certain amount of time in *military service* as well as in various industrial and mechanical activities. Naturally, most of them stayed in the kind of service to which they were best fitted (and the mechanical conveniences of the age made them practically as efficient as men in nearly all lines) unless they married. Then they adopted home-making as their career, and were subject to call for military or other service only in case of emergency.

Wilma, who had self-reliance, fearlessness and stamina, even beyond the high average of her 25th Century sisters, had naturally remained in the military service, for which her talents eminently fitted her, and into this same service I naturally gravitated.

WEAPONS OF THE 25TH CENTURY

The weapons and equipment of the military service were most interesting to me. Men and girls wore close-fitting uniforms of a *synthetically fabricated material,* not a woven cloth, that had the consistency of soft leather and yet was most difficult to cut or tear. For service in cold climates, uniform cloth was *electronically* treated to radiate inward a continuous glow of heat, while the outside surface was heat resistant. For warm climates the cloth was given a spongy texture for aeration, and a high ratio of heat conductivity.

The jumping belt was, of course, a part of the regular equipment, as was the close-fitting helmet, of the same material as the uniforms, into which were built the tiny receivers of the individual radio-phone sets that enabled an officer to give commands to his entire force, scattered over an area miles in extent, or to converse with a single scout individually from a distance.

Of the weapons, the *rocket pistol* was the nearest thing to the firearms of the 20th Century, I knew. It was very much like an old automatic, except that its magazine was much larger, and the propelling charge was in a tiny cartridge case that travelled *with* the highly explosive bullet instead of remaining in the pistol, giving flatter trajectory and greater range. And some of these bullets had explosive power equal to artillery shells of the 20th Century.

There were, of course, *rocket guns;* great squat cannon from which leaped self-propelling shells capable of shattering an area of a mile or more in radius.

The *telev-eye,* used either as a weapon of destruction or for scouting, was an aerial torpedo, its weight eliminated by inertron counterbalancing, radio-controlled, with a great "eye" or lens, behind which was located a television transmitter that relayed back to its operator, who was safely entrenched miles in the rear, the picture which this "eye" picked up. Once the telev-eye picked up a fugitive aircraft, that ship was doomed, for no ship could outmaneuver or out-speed these terrible projectiles of destruction, which were so small that they could seldom be hit by enemy guns.

Another most efficient weapon for short range work was the *paralysis gun.* This was a pistol, from which flashed a faintly visible, crackling beam of energy vibrations that temporarily paralyzed certain brain centers. A person hit by this ray instantly dropped rigid and paralyzed, to remain that way for minutes or hours, and then recover with no worse effects than a bad headache.

But to me one of the most amazing weapons of the 25th Century was the *lightning gun.* This wasn't really a gun at all, though it was called such from its general appearance. It was an electronic generator and projector. From it flashed forth an invisible beam of carrier-wave oscillations along which could be sent a stupendous electrical charge. Its use was against aircraft. It was only necessary to focus the beam on the unsuspecting target, and then flash along it an electrical charge of opposite polarity to that in the clouds. When that ship later neared a cloud, it was struck by lightning. Obviously great care had to be taken in the operation of the lightning gun, or the gun itself might pull a bolt from the clouds. It could only be used under certain atmospheric conditions. Batteries of these lightning guns were stationed at strategic points over the country and along the sea coast, co-ordinated to "fire" all at once, in groups, or singly, as necessity required.

AMAZING CITIES

I entered into the life of the 25th Century with a mighty zest. On every hand were marvels almost unbelievable. Cities of towering pinnacles. Others that had been roofed over with great domes of *metalloglass,* a transparent product with a strength greater than steel. And still others that were in reality one single great building, spreading for miles with mazes of thoroughfares, internal corridors and external galleries, along which shot automatically controlled *floating cars.*

The lift in these cars was furnished by an over-balance of inertron, but the *cosmo-magnetic* grip of the guide rails embedded in the pavements held them down to within twelve inches of the ground. One had only to enter one of these cars, locate his destination as to avenue, cross-corridor and level on the triple dial and then relax. An amazingly complex system of car and power-house controls guided the vehicle promptly and safely by the shortest available route to the recorded destination.

But I never ceased to wonder at the amazing number of these marvels whose real beginnings, back in the 20th Century, I could actually recall.

Radio? It was basically and fundamentally woven into the whole fabric and structure of the 25th Century civilization. But *such* radio! Radio that embraced myriad types and varieties of *electronic, sub-electronic, infra-magnetic* and *cosmic* oscillations. Matter could be formed out of force with it. And even as the 20th Century scientists conceived and executed great scientific advances, so the 25th Century scientists to an even greater extent developed new, *synthetic elements* of strange properties, not existing naturally in any part of the universe. Inertron, for instance, was one of these. It had weight; but its weight caused it to fall *up* instead of *down.*

RED MONGOL TERROR

However, despite the development of five vivid centuries of scientific achievement, man's own social and moral progress still lagged behind the progress of his creations. True, the average was far higher than it had been in the 20th Century, but there were on the face of the globe races whose advance in material civilization had been accompanied by moral and spiritual decay.

There were, for instance, the terrible *Red Mongols,* cruel, greedy and unbelievably ruthless, who for a time, all too long, utterly crushed a large part of humanity in a slavery frightful to contemplate.

In their great battle craft, sliding across the sky as though riding on columns of scintillating light, they drove like a scourge over all North America, with their terrible *disintegrator rays* blasting men and entire cities into nothingness. Where these beams fell, matter simply ceased to exist, and an instantaneous flicker was sufficient to gash the landscape with channels and canals sometimes a hundred or more feet deep and leave iridescent, vitreous scars where soft earth had been before.

The disintegrator ray, however, became one of the most useful tools of 25th Century civilization in small projector form, with which tunnels could be bored and automatically finished with a hard vitreous surface with amazing rapidity, or with which refuse could be most economically destroyed, either by use of the hand machines or permanent installations.

Wilma and I saw service in the war against these cruel Red Mongols and played an exciting part in the many fierce battles with them.

KILLER KANE AND ARDALA

But even among the more advanced races criminals still existed, and it was the density of Wilma and myself to frustrate the evil plans of certain super-criminals, *Killer Kane* and his companion, *Ardala,* and so win their undying hatred and enmity.

Wilma, like other youngsters of all centuries, had had her dreams, and unfortunately these had centered lightly at one time on a man who then had an unblemished reputation for integrity and ability, but she had broken with him instantly when she realized the potential evil that lay beneath his vivid personality. This man was Killer Kane.

My coming and the interest Wilma showed in me had fanned Kane's smouldering

resentment into a seething flame of hate. He later plunged into a criminal career of such utter daring and magnificent proportions as to be unequalled in the annals of two centuries. And though the beautiful, sleek adventuress, Ardala, was his constant and capable partner in crime, Kane never forgave nor forgot the wound to his vanity nor his consuming passion for revenge.

And Ardala, though giving Killer Kane all the affection and loyalty of which her fierce, deceitful, feline nature was capable, suffered constantly the pangs of burning jealousy, and in consequence matched his hatred of Wilma and me with an enmity for us no less deadly because of her subtle talents.

Throughout the Earth, and even beyond, into the vast voids of space, and other strange planets, Wilma's struggle and mine with Killer Kane and Ardala was fated to continue.

CONTROL OF SPACE SHIPS

For interplanetary travel *was* an accomplished fact in the 25th Century. Even back in 1933 aviation engineers constructed a craft to fly the *stratosphere,* that upper section of the Earth's atmosphere in which the air is too rare for breathing, and from which its density declines gradually to the vacuum of interplanetary space.

The first *space ships* in which we, Wilma and I, feeling infinitely less than microscopic, dared the immensity of outer void, were rocket propelled. In a vacuum, whirling fan blades are futile for propulsion, for there is nothing for the blade to pull or push against. But the rocket, so to speak, provides "air" against which to push. The blazing gas, roaring out of the rocket tube, piles up against that which was emitted the preceding instant, and has not yet had time to expand to extreme rarefaction. The reaction of this piling up shoves the ship ahead. And since there is no air friction in space to retard the ship a single impulse would give it a momentum that would continue forever, or until it was altered by some such event as entering the gravitational field of some planet, or colliding with a planetoid. Such speed, however, would be very slow, and the enormous distances to be covered in space made it imperative to attain speeds undreamed of in the antiquated days of 1933—five hundreds years in the dim past.

INTERPLANETARY NAVIGATION

But with a continuous blast such as these ships used, they roared away from Earth at constantly accelerating speed. A rate of acceleration somewhat less than that of a falling body on Earth (and even back in 1933 experiences of aviators and parachute jumpers had proved the human system can stand the acceleration of gravity) but which constantly continued for even a few hours produced terrific speed.

And as the space ship was so constructed that its *bow* was its *top,* and its *stern* the *base,* this *upward acceleration* had the effect of pressing its passengers *downward* against its decks with something not far from equivalent to the force of gravity. At the half-way mark the ship, now floating through space at frightful speed, was gently swung about by small side-blasts, steadied with its *base* pointed in the direction of travel. And so for the second half of the journey the main blasts acted to *decelerate* the ship gradually, and at the same rate as the former acceleration. This deceleration substituted for gravity in the same way, and by the time the ship arrived at its planet of destination a few days, or a few months later, its speed was so reduced that it could safely enter the atmosphere and ride down on its rocket blasts to a gentle landing.

The controls of these space ships had been so carefully worked out by the scientific engineers—and the ships themselves so nicely balanced that a crew of two men—or girls for that matter—could easily operate one of the gigantic crafts.

OLD DOCTOR HUER—SCIENTIST EXTRAORDINARY

But this conquest of vast distances had not been possible until Old Doctor Huer, foremost scientist of the 25th Century, with whom Wilma and I were associated in many adventures, had invented a method of creating *matter in gaseous form from the energy impulses of sunlight and cosmic rays,* with sufficient speed and in sufficient quanity to serve as rocket fuel. For no ship could hold enough rocket fuel for an entire interplanetary trip. It had to be derived from some outside source en route.

NON-RECOIL ENERGY

Huer, an amazing man for his age (I knew him to be over seventy), an indefatigable scientist and an irrepressible adventurer, also invented and developed the practical application of *non-recoil energy,* or as it was sometimes called, *"one-way energy,"* by which a man might literally "lift himself by his bootstraps."

The non-recoil energy tube was a small affair, resembling an ancient electric flashlight. It emitted a beam of energy which acted with controllable "push" against anything at which it was directed, but without any recoil whatever against the user. The principle was not dissimilar to that of shock and rebound absorbers on ancient automobiles or the recoil devices of ancient cannons, but it was a matter of carefully balanced electronic and sub-cosmic energy control rather than one of mechanical construction.

Curiously, a man might hold one of these tubes pointed upward in one hand, and placing his other hand over the projector lens, rise on it as though holding on to a strap.

Force tubes, of course, had been known for a long time, but in these the push was equal at both ends of the tube. They were, as a matter of fact, almost identical with the powerful *repeller rays* on which the dreaded air-raiding ships of the Red Mongols rode, beams of faint light that pushed downward with terrific force against the ground, and upward with equal force against the keel of the ship generating them. The Mongols maneuvered their ships by the simple method of altering the slant of these rays. Slanted astern, they drove the ship forward, and vice versa.

Huer's non-recoil energy, of course, had innumerable applications. It was ideal motive power for all kinds of vehicles, aircraft and space ships. And in *industry* it had a thousand applications.

ECONOMY OF LABOR

Had we not been plunged by circumstances, and the deadly hatred of Killer Kane and Ardala, into one desperate adventure after another, we could have found a never-ending interest in the adroit uses to which this convenient power of Dr. Huer's was put in the daily industrial life of the people. I had seen men punch holes in the hardest steel with a device little larger than a screwdriver, and with no more effort than a housewife might use in cutting biscuits out of a slab of dough.

COMMUNITY KITCHENS

There was very little home cooking, however, in the 25th Century. At least not in the cities; and only a small percentage of the population was required to run the *farms.*

A marvelous system of conveyors led from the *community kitchens* to every apartment. One could order his meal a la carte or table d'hote. In due course a wall panel would slide back, and a "floating table" would ease gently into the room, safely balanced on *"lifters"* of inertron, with everything in readiness. It required but the pressure of a finger to guide this to any part of the room where one chose to sit, and anchor it by lowering the counterbalancing weights underneath it. When hunger was satisfied, it only remained to push the table back and close the panel on it. The kitchens themselves were mazes of ingenious devices for handling the food and dishes, which for mechanical considerations were square rather than round.

SYNTHETIC FOOD

But I never could cultivate a taste for certain of the foods that were the product of synthetic laboratories. For by this time less than half of all foodstuffs came from the farms. Men had learned to create the most nourishing of foods from minerals alone, by a process of dis-integration and electronic recombination into complicated organic substances easily assimilated by the human system.

VANISHED FARMS AND ROADS

Indeed, most of the land was no longer under cultivation, for an area of a few miles radius around each city was all that was needed for agricultural purposes, so much of the bulk food was produced synthetically. In consequence the *forests* were growing again, and vast sections

that had been highly farmed in the old days were now stretches of woodland and prairie untouched by the hand of man, for even freight was not carried by rail, and there was no use for *roads,* although over the beauty of this wilderness the *air routes* hummed with the swift passage of freight and passenger traffic from one center of population to another, and occasionally outing parties or forest patrols could be seen leaping lightly over hill and dale with the aid of their jumping belts.

THE RED PLANET

But my interests were not confined to Earth. Stranger still than this world of the 25th Century were those other worlds to which my adventures carried me.

Mars, with its clear sparkling air, its cloudless skies and its pale, greenish yellow sunshine, its vast red deserts and great canals, many of them ten to twenty miles wide, sweeping in straight lines and immense curves, to form fascinating patterns when seen from the upper air levels; its peculiar beasts, its occasional jagged mountain ranges of crystal-clear quartz, and its amazing people, so like those of Earth in most respects, but so unlike them in certain of the customs and mental reactions.

MOONS OF SATURN

The *Moons of Saturn,* a little galaxy of worlds, some larger and some smaller than our dead, airless moon of Earth, were so close together that they appeared (from the inner ones) like great pale discs sliding perpetually in confusing orbits across a blue-grey dome. And *Saturn* itself, always an amazing sight as it filled half the sky with its great rings looped around it. On these worlds I never knew whether to call it night or day, for the reflected light from Saturn was almost as great, although soft and diffuse, as the hard, clear light from the distant sun; and that from the other moons was much like the light of Saturn itself.

THE LIQUID-AIR OCEANS OF JUPITER

Jupiter, another amazing planet, where men lived on vast plateaus that were in reality the tops of mountain ranges *thousands of miles* above the valleys, in the mysterious depths of which the blue air liquefied under a pressure almost too great for the mind of man to comprehend. No Jovian had ever plumbed the depths of those valleys. No craft *could* descend into them more than a fraction of the way. No material existed in the universe of which a vessel could be made that would not crush like an eggshell under that super-pressure. So Jovian life was confined to the mountain tops that were continents surrounded by "seas" of air, across which the intercontinental flyers flashed on their weary journeys; for the distances were vast. Jupiter has a diameter about ten times that of Earth, and many an intrepid explorer has been lost thereon.

THE EROS MYSTERY

Then there was *Eros,* the cigar-shaped planetoid that swung end over end in an orbit beyond that of Mars, and on, and *in* which Wilma and I found things that staggered and shattered our imaginations.

ATLANTIS, THE CITY UNDER THE SEA

But there were wonders on Earth too, undreamed of back in the 20th Century, even though hints of them remained in old forgotten legends. The legend of *Atlantis,* for instance, the city and continent that sank beneath the sea in prehistoric times, and of whose original inhabitants many of the Caucasian races are descendants.

Atlantis still existed, under the ocean, inhabited by men who through the countless ages had become amphibian, who were equally at home in the artificially ventilated corridors and chambers of their submarine city, or in the water of the sea surrounding it, who had a civilization no less advanced, but strangely different from that of Earth's land races, from whom they had been living apart for eons.

It was Wilma and I who "discovered" Atlantis. It was there that one of our most desperate struggles with Killer Kane and Ardala occurred. Far beneath the surface of the Atlantic, these two super-criminals succeeded in balking our every more. However, it was we who finally succeeded in—but that is a story in itself.

THE ASTERITES

And there were the *Asterites,* tiny men not more than a foot tall, who came from outer space, and began with deadly determination their campaign of conquest and destruction of the planet Earth. And it was Wilma and I who bore the brunt of their first attack, with consequences that could not have been foreseen.

AND SO, it was among such surroundings and events as the foregoing that Buck Rogers, the lithe, sinewy, 20th Century youth who by a strange trick of fate jumped the time gap from the the 20th to the 25th Century, and Wilma, that dashing, fearless lovely girl of the new day, lived and loved and struggled, both joyously and mightily, to overcome the evil that not only for the World, but for the Universe, was personified in the ruthlessly bitter, magnificent wickedness of Killer Kane, and the evil that lay in the heart of Ardala.

Phil Nowlan
Dick Calkins

Chicago
February 8, 1932

1
MEETING THE MONGOLS

BUCK ROGERS IN THE 25th CENTURY

1

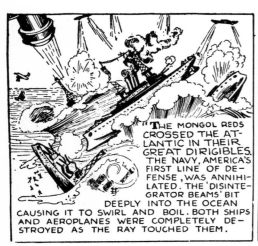

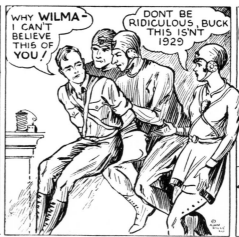
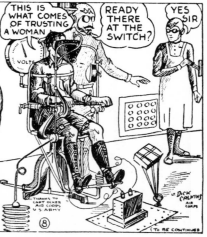

MEETING THE MONGOLS

3

MEETING THE MONGOLS

MEETING THE MONGOLS

SENT BY THE MONGOL VICEROY OF CHICAGO, WHO HOPED TO CAPTURE WILMA FOR THE EMPEROR'S HAREM, CAME SOFTLY TO EARTH. "TWO OF YOU SNEAK UP AND GAS THE SENTRIES· WE MUST STEAL THAT GIRL OUT OF THE HOSPITAL WITHOUT RAISING AN ALARM· THE AIR RAIDER"

"A MONGOL RAID—TURN OUT THE GUARD!" "QUICK! BACK TO THE SHIP WITH HER!" I HAD BEEN SITTING IN THE MOONLIGHT, DEPRESSED BY WILMA'S DISPLEASURE, WHEN I SAW FIGURES COMING OUT OF THE CAMOUFLAGED HOSPITAL.

"I MUST CATCH THEM—I MUST" TRY AS I WOULD, I COULD NOT OVERTAKE THE RAIDERS, FOR I HAD LAID ASIDE MY JUMPING BELT, AND MY ROCKET PISTOL, TOO.

"HELP! BUCK HELP!" "BACK TO YOUR FOREST KENNEL, DOG!" "WILMA" (25) (TO BE CONTINUED)

"WILMA GOT ONE CHANCE TO USE HER RADIOPHONE, SIR· THE MONGOLS ARE HEADING NORTHWEST, TOWARD VANCOUVER." "GIVE ME A SHIP, GENERAL—I MUST FOLLOW THEM!" "POSITIVELY NO, YOU COULDN'T CATCH THEM· BESIDES, I HAVE NO PLANES TO WASTE"

"INSUBORDINATION OR NOT—I'M GOING TO RESCUE WILMA" BITTERLY DISAPPOINTED, I LEFT HEADQUARTERS, CRAZED WITH GRIEF, AND FINDING THE ORG'S ONLY SCOUT SHIP UNGUARDED, MADE MY DECISION IN AN INSTANT.

"WHAT A SWELL PLACE FOR A DEAD STICK LANDING!" I FLEW NORTHWEST FOR HOURS, FIGHTING FOR EVERY OUNCE OF SPEED, WHEN SUDDENLY MY MOTOR CONKED COLD.

"COULD THERE BE A TOUGHER BREAK? GOSH, I'M LUCKY I DIDN'T CRACK UP! THIS MUST BE BRITISH COLUMBIA—OR ELSE." (26) TO BE CONTINUED

"THE WORST OF IT IS, I DON'T KNOW WHETHER OR NOT THE MONGOLS HELD TO THEIR COURSE" FORCED DOWN IN BRITISH COLUMBIA, I SET FRANTICALLY TO WORK REPAIRING MY MOTOR.

"HERE'S LUCK ON JUMPING BELTS! MUST BE CANADIAN ORGMEN."

"MIGHTY GOOD OF YOU TO HELP GET MY MOTOR IN RUNNING ORDER· SO YOU'RE VANCOUVER MEN, EH?" "YES, WE WERE TRANSFERRED FROM MONTREAL· OUR SCOUTS REPORT A MONGOL SHIP, SUCH AS YOU DESCRIBE, FLYING SOUTH, PROBABLY HEADING FOR SAN FRANCISCO OR LOS ANGELES."

"NOW, BABY, STRUT YOUR STUFF! STRAIGHT TO THE IMPERIAL CITY· I SEE IT ALL NOW—THOSE BUMS ARE TAKING WILMA TO THE EMPEROR." (27) (TO BE CONTINUED)

"IF I CAN HOLD THIS SPEED, I MAY CATCH THEM BEFORE THEY REACH LOS ANGELES" AS I FLEW SOUTH, IN PURSUIT OF THE MONGOL SHIP IN WHICH WILMA WAS A PRISONER, I PASSED NEAR THE RUINS OF ANCIENT SEATTLE—THEN THE REMAINS OF TACOMA AND PORTLAND SLID PAST.

BUT LUCK WAS AGAINST ME· I RAN INTO DIRTY WEATHER, AND BEFORE LONG FOUND MYSELF IN THE GRIP OF A BLINDING HAILSTORM. "IF THIS KEEPS UP, I'LL BE FORCED DOWN· WONDER WHERE I AM?"

"THIS COMPASS MUST BE COO-COO! I'M OFF MY COURSE!" STICKING HER NOSE UP, I COAXED MY SHIP ABOVE THE STORM AND AGAIN TURNED SOUTH, WHEN—

"WELL, HERE GOES FOR A MEMBERSHIP IN TH' CATERPILLAR CLUB" THE JOY STICK SNAPPED VICIOUSLY TO THE RIGHT· A CONTROL WIRE HAD PARTED, AND I WENT A·W·O·L· (28) (TO BE CONTINUED)

7

DESPERATELY I FOUGHT, SCRAMBLED, AND THREW MYSELF TOWARD THE SIDE OF THE SLIDE, AND FINALLY FLUNG CLEAR OF IT.

THAT CAME NEAR BEING MY FINISH!

BUT THE "NEVER-SAY-DIE" SPIRIT OF MY PIONEER ANCESTORS URGED ME TO CARRY ON.

BY MID AFTERNOON, I FELL BESIDE A BRACKISH DESERT WATER HOLE. THIS REVIVED ME AND I STUMBLED ON.

AS THE DAY WANED, THE EVENING GALE, RUSHING THROUGH SOME GAP IN THE RIDGE, SWEPT A STORM OF DESERT DUST THAT ALMOST BURIED ME. (TO BE CONTINUED)

WHILE BUCK WAS FIGHTING FOR HIS LIFE ON THE DESERT—

WILMA FOUND MONGOLIAN CITY LIFE NOT UNPLEASANT FOR A PROSPECTIVE FAVORITE OF THE EMPEROR.

IS THE TEMPERATURE PLEASING TO MY LADY?

OH, QUITE! ESPECIALLY AFTER THE OLD SWIMMING HOLE.

WHAT A DELICIOUS BREAKFAST! THESE SYNTHETIC FOODS ARE MARVELOUS—MOJAH, SEE WHO IS AT THE DOOR.

KNOCK KNOCK KNOCK

HIS IMPERIAL MAJESTY REQUESTS THE PRESENCE OF MY LADY WILMA TO REHEARSE HER COMING INVESTITURE AS FAVORITE.

FAVORITE? DON'T BE SILLY!

(TO BE CONTINUED)

BUDDHA SPEED THE DAY WHEN THOU WILT BE MINE OH LOVELY ONE.

THE MONGOL EMPEROR BIDED HIS TIME UNTIL THE AGE-OLD CEREMONIES SHOULD BE COMPLETED.

WHAT IS THIS, A MUSICAL COMEDY?

WILMA WAS REQUIRED TO REHEARSE THE CEREMONY AT WHICH THE EMPEROR HOPED TO MAKE HER HIS FAVORITE, ALTHOUGH SHE NEVER INTENDED TO GO THROUGH WITH IT.

IN THE MEANTIME

THE WIND WAS LIKE A ROARING BLAST FROM A FURNACE, AND THE SAND CUT LIKE A THOUSAND TINY KNIVES. (TO BE CONTINUED)

STILL, IT'S THE ONLY WAY. I HAVE TO CLIMB IT.

I WEATHERED THE SANDSTORM, BUT ONLY TO REACH AN UNSURMOUNTABLE CLIFF.

CAN THAT BE A WAY OUT?

AFTER UNSUCCESSFULLY TRYING TO SCALE THE BARRIER, I FOLLOWED ALONG ITS BASE, UNTIL—

SURE! WE KIN USE HIS CLOTHES.

HA! LOOK! LET'S SOCK HIM!

I HAD INDEED FOUND A PASS THROUGH THE RIDGE, BUT WHEN I EMERGED FROM THE OTHER END———

TO BE CONTINUED

MEETING THE MONGOLS

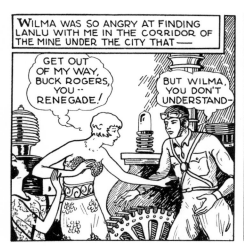

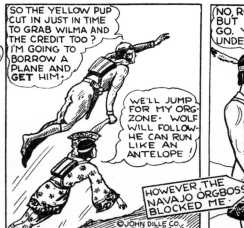

BUCK ROGERS IN THE 25th CENTURY

GRIEF STRICKEN IN MY BELIEF THAT I HAD LOST WILMA, I FALSELY IMAGINED—

WILMA! AT LAST

AH KILLER!

© JOHN DILLE CO.

BUT THE NAVAJO BOSS WAS SYMPATHETIC.

I'LL RADIOPHONE YOUR ORGZONE AND TRY TO GET YOUR RELEASE.

AW, WHAT'S THE USE OF ANYTHING!

WHAT'S THAT AN OUTLAW! OH, I SAY, MAGEE THAT DOESN'T SEEM FAIR!

ON THE DEMAND OF BOSS MAGEE, BUT AGAINST MY OWN WILL, I HEREBY INDICT YOU AS A DESERTER AND A SPY. PREPARE FOR TRIAL!

(TO BE CONTINUED)

CAPTAIN ROGERS, THE RADIOPHONE EVIDENCE IS CONCLUSIVE. THIS COUNCIL FINDS YOU GUILTY OF DESERTION AND ESPIONAGE

THE NAVAJO ORGMEN, BEING DESCENDANTS OF THE NAVAJO INDIANS, HAD PRESERVED CERTAIN ANCIENT TRIBAL CUSTOMS, AND AT MY TRIAL THE COURT OFFICIALS WRAPPED THEMSELVES IN CEREMONIAL BLANKETS.

YOUR OWN ORGBOSS DEMANDS THAT YOU BE BRANDED AN OUTLAW! HENCEFORTH, YOU MAY LEGALLY BE SHOT ON SIGHT. VAMOSE!

BLIND FOOLS! AND WILMA BELIEVES IT, TOO!

BROKEN AND DISGRACED, THROUGH MY LOVE FOR WILMA, I FACED A TERRIBLE FUTURE.

© JOHN DILLE CO.

AN OUTCAST! WELL, IT WAS WHITE OF THAT REDSKIN TO LET ME KEEP MY JUMPING HARNESS

(TO BE CONTINUED)

ME AN OUTLAW! THAT'S A HOT ONE.

STRIPPED OF ALL MY EQUIPMENT EXCEPT MY JUMPING BELT, I WAS DRIVEN INTO THE DESERT.

I'M GETTING NOWHERE FAST. I—I GUESS I'LL LIE DOWN A MINUTE.

AFTER HOURS OF STEADY JUMPING UNDER A PITILESS SUN.

AN ORGMAN! I HOPE HIS BOOTS FIT ME.

DEADER'N A DOORNAIL

© JOHN DILLE CO.

HE AIN'T DEAD!

I'LL SAY I'M NOT, YOU RATS!

(TO BE CONTINUED)

THE GOOD OLD ONE-TWO PUNCH I HAD LEARNED IN THE ARMY DROPPED ONE OF THE DESERT RATS COLD. A RIGHT HOOK TO THE JAW AND THE OTHER HEARD THE BIRDIES SING.

ZOWIE! RIGHT ON THE BUTTON!

OH WILMA, DARLING IT'S WONDERFUL TO HAVE YOU BACK.

HELEN, TELL ME WHAT'S BEEN GOING ON!

IN THE MEANTIME WILMA HAD BEEN TAKEN HOME BY KILLER KANE.

© JOHN DILLE CO.

—AND SO AT MAGEE'S DEMAND THE NAVAJOS OUTLAWED BUCK!

WHY, WHAT DO YOU MEAN?

SHE MEANS I GOT MAGEE TO OUTLAW THAT DIRTY MONGOL SPY, ROGERS.

OH! OH! WHAT A FOOL I'VE BEEN!

(TO BE CONTINUED)

14

MEETING THE MONGOLS

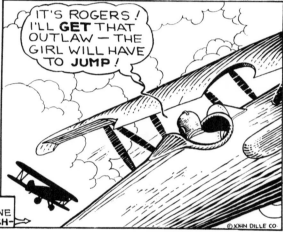

THE CYCLONE KID WAS STRONG BUT HE HAD NO SCIENCE, SO I QUICKLY POLISHED HIM OFF.

YOU WIN STRANGER. I DON'T WANT THE GAL!

ANYBODY ELSE?

I SHORE RECKON I CAN ACCOMODATE YUH.

HERE'S WHERE YUH HITS TH' ALKALI!

TO BE CONTINUED

AS LARIAT LUKE'S LOOP WHISTLED OVER MY SHOULDERS, I LEAPED—

WHO'S NEXT?

FELLA, WE AIM TO GIVE YA WHAT'S COMIN' TO YA.

(TO BE CONTINUED)

—BUT—BUT

—THAT'S OUR CODE, BOSS

MY VICTORY OVER LARIAT LUKE MADE ME BOSS OF THE GANG.

I DIDN'T KNOW ANYONE COULD BE SO WONDERFUL, BUCK.

NEITHER DID I

SAY-Y-BOSS, THERE'S ONE OUTLAW YUH CAN'T LICK—IN THIS HYAR CORRAL.

BUCK DEAR, DON'T RIDE THAT BRUTE—HE'LL KILL YOU.

IT'S GOT TO BE DONE HONEY—OR THEY'LL CALL ME YELLOW.

TO BE CON'T.

NOW *BUCK!* OLD HOSS THAT'S MY FIRST NAME.

C'MON, SLEEPY! SHOW SOME PEP!

FOOLED YOU THAT TIME, DIDN'T I?

ALTHOUGH I WAS NO BRONCO BUSTER, MY JUMPING BELT KEPT ME FROM BEING THROWN TO THE GROUND.

EASY, NOW, OLD BOY

THE SAVAGE ANIMAL WAS FRANTIC DISPITE HIS EFFORTS, I MERELY FLOATED ABOVE HIM.

(TO BE CONTINUED)

MEETING THE MONGOLS

"HOW DID YOU LIKE **THOSE** ONIONS?"

"ATTA BOY, BUCK!"

THANKS TO MY JUMPING BELT, I FINALLY WORE THE OUTLAW HORSE DOWN. MY LEADERSHIP IN THE GANG WAS ASSURED.

"TRY THIS ON, ONE OF YOU."

"NOTHIN' DOIN' BOSS — NONE O' THEM NEW FANGLED DOO-DADS FER US"

I TRIED IN VAIN TO INTEREST MY FOLLOWERS IN THE JUMPING BELT.

"AREN'T YOU JUST THR-R-RILLED?"

"I ADMIT IT. HE'S SWEET"

AND WILMA'S NEW FRIENDS TEASED HER ABOUT OUR COMING MARRIAGE.

"HEY! SASHAY OUT HERE, SOMEBODY! LARIAT LUKE'S BEEN VENTILATED!"

—BUT TRAGEDY INTERRUPTED—

LT. DICK CALKINS AIR CORPS RES

73.

(TO BE CONTINUED)

"WHO SHOT YOU, LUKE?"

"TWO OF BOSS TABB'S MEN GOT ME—— AH—H—"

SO I RADIOPHONED BOSS TABB WHO HEADED A NEIGHBORING ORG, BUT—

"JUSTICE! THAT'S A LAUGH! YOU **OUT-LAWS** HAVE NO RIGHTS."

"IS **THAT** SO? WE'LL SEE!"

AS SOON AS WE COULD ORGANIZE, I LED A RAIDING PARTY AGAINST TABB'S ORGZONE.

LT. DICK CALKINS AIR CORPS RES

74.

(TO BE CONTINUED)

BOSS TABB KNEW WE OUTLAWS HAD LITTLE MODERN EQUIPMENT, SO HE DIDN'T FEAR US MUCH, BUT HE UNDERESTIMATED THE SPEED OF OUR HORSES, SO—

—WE TOOK HIM AND HIS MEN BY SURPRISE

"TABB, YOU ARE TO SEND US THREE HUNDRED JUMPING BELTS"

"—AND HANG THEM KILLERS"

"OH, ALL RIGHT, BUT YOU'LL PAY HEAVY FOR THIS"

"RIDE HIM, COWGIRL!"

"HE'LL BE A HIGH HORSE IN A MINUTE!"

WHEN THE BELTS WERE DELIVERED WILMA AND I TRIED AN EXPERIMENT. COULD **HORSES** AS WELL AS MEN LEAP WITH THEIR AID?

LT. DICK CALKINS AIR CORPS RES.

75.

(TO BE CONTINUED)

THE HORSE MADE A SUCCESSFUL LEAP OF A FULL 500 FEET.

THIS GOT MY FOLLOWERS INTERESTED IN THE "NEWFANGLED" BELTS, AND, WHILE I WAS ORGANIZING A "FLYING SQUADRON"—

"'PHONE US FROM MARS, HENRY"

"DON'T, BOYS, DON'T SEND ME UP! NO-NO-OH MY ——"

SOME OF THE BOYS PLAYED A PRACTICAL JOKE ON HANK, THE COOK.

"HELP!"

"HAVE A GOOD TRIP HANK"

"BOYS! THIS ISN'T FUNNY—IT'S **MURDER!** GIVE ME FOUR JUMPING BELTS, QUICK!"

LT. DICK CALKINS AIR CORPS RES.

76.

(TO BE CONTINUED)

BUCK ROGERS IN THE 25th CENTURY

20

MEETING THE MONGOLS

21

BUCK ROGERS IN THE 25th CENTURY

I LEAPED TO THE TOP OF A TALL TREE, TO GET A VIEW OF THE ONRUSHING AIR FLEET.

MEANWHILE THE MONGOL CRUISER HAD LANDED TO TAKE KILLER KANE AND HIS BEATEN TROOPS ABOARD. AT THIS MOMENT MacGREGOR'S ROCKET SHIPS DIVED UPON THEM WITH INCREDIBLE SPEED, TAKING THEM BY SURPRISE.

A FURIOUS AND AMAZING COMBAT RAGED. SLOWLY BUT SURELY THE MONGOL COLOSSUS WAS REDUCED TO A TANGLED MASS OF MEN AND METAL.

ROGERS, I KNOW YE FOR AN OOT'LAW, BUT A BONNY FIGHTER, SO IF YE'LL JOIN MA AIR-GUARD, I'LL PUT IN A GUID WORD FOR YE AT HEADQUARTERS

(TO BE CONTINUED)

HOW ABOOT IT?

MacGREGOR, YOU'RE A PRINCE. WILL WE ACCEPT? CAN A DUCK SWIM?

RIGHTO. YE'RE NOW UNDER MY COMMAND. FAIR-R-RST CATCH ME THAT TRAITOR KILLER KANE. JUMP NOW!

WE'LL USE OUR FLYING CAVALRY

HOW'LL WE EVER FIND HIM IN THESE CANYONS?

STRAPPING ON ONE OF MY HORSE'S JUMPING BELTS AND KNOTTING A LARIAT AROUND MY WAIST, I DID SOME AERIAL OBSERVATION.

THERE GOES KANE!

(TO BE CONTINUED)

YOU'RE AT THE END OF YOUR ROPE NOW, KANE

I GIVE UP!

LIGHTENED BY THE ANTI-GRAVITY BELTS, OUR HORSES, IN GREAT LEAPS, OVERTOOK KILLER KANE.

WHAT'S THIS FEDERATION MacGREGOR SPEAKS OF

IT'S A UNION OF CANADIAN AND ATLANTIC ORGZONES. I GUESS IT'S GROWN WHILE WE'VE BEEN OUTLAWS

HERE'S THE SNEAKING TRAITOR, SIR.

I ASK A SOLDIER'S DEATH. SHOOT ME BUT DON'T HANG ME!

I'LL DO NEITHER. I'M SENDING YE BACK TO YOUR MONGOL EMPEROR WITH THIS MESSAGE. 'TIS IMPOR-R-RTANT!

A MESSAGE?

WHAT ABOUT?

(TO BE CONTINUED)

I SENT KANE WI' AN ULTIMATUM TO HIS MONGOL EMPEROR THAT, THE FEDERATION WILL STAND FOR NO MORE RAIDS ON ORGZONES

ALL THE ORGZONES EAST OF ST. LOUIS AND IN CANADA HAVE JOINED THE FEDERATION

THEN I MUST SEEM TO AGREE. I ACCEPT THE TRUCE, BUT IN THE END I WILL DESTROY THEM!

AND WHEN THE TRAITOR WAS LANDED IN THE IMPERIAL CITY.

WELL, BUCK, US OUTLAWS WILL MISS YOU AND YORE GAL.

DROP US A PITCHER POST CARD

I HATE TO LEAVE ALL THESE NICE MEN.

MEANWHILE, WILMA AND I WERE RE-OUTFITTED BY MacGREGOR

OH BOY! WILL I BE GLAD TO SEE THE CITY!

ME TOO! I'M FED UP ON GREAT OPEN SPACES!

SO AS MEMBERS OF THE MacGREGOR AIR GUARD, OF TORONTO, WE ROCKETED FOR NIAGARA, THE NORTH AMERICAN CAPITAL. (TO BE CONT'D)

MEETING THE MONGOLS

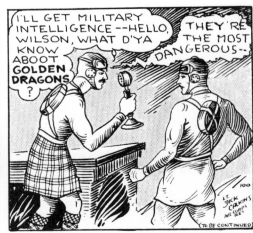

MEETING THE MONGOLS

Z-ZZIP-P

MY CONCEALED OPPONENT REVEALED HIS POSITION TO ME, AND—

A TREE TOAD! HE'S CHIRPED HIS LAST CHIRP

I NEATLY DROPPED THE MONGOL SNIPER.

©JOHN DILLE CO.

AT THIS MOMENT OM-KA-ZORIL AT WORK IN HIS LABORATORY LOOKED UP AND SAW—

DANGER SPIES

HO! GOLDEN DRAGONS TO ARMS!

LT. DICK CALKINS AIR CORPS RES 105.

(TO BE CONTINUED)

GET THAT MAN!

WARNED OF MY APPROACH, OM-KA-ZORIL MARSHALLED HIS FOLLOWERS, WHO SPREAD OUT IN FANLIKE FORMATION AS THEY CAME TOWARD ME

I'M BADLY OUTNUMBERED! NOTHING BUT STRATEGY WILL PULL ME OUT OF THIS HOLE

I SAW THEM AS I EMERGED FROM THE TREES AND CAME IN SIGHT OF THE LABORATORY.

©JOHN DILLE CO.

HERE'S WHERE I DO SOME GROUND STRAFING!

I JUMPED BEYOND RANGE OF THEIR DISINTEGRATOR RAYS AND OPENED AN EFFECTIVE ROCKET FIRE FROM THE AIR.

LT. DICK CALKINS A.C.R. 106

(TO BE CONTINUED)

WHEN THE SMOKE CLEARED AWAY ONLY OM-KA-ZORIL STOOD BETWEEN ME AND THE INFERNAL MACHINE I HAD COME TO DESTROY

I'LL BLAST YOU WITH THE GIANT BEAM—I'LL—

YOU'LL WHAT? YOU'LL SURRENDER OR PUSH UP DAISIES.

WELL, IF YOU MUST HAVE IT, TAKE IT

CLICK

-LICK-

BUT THE MAGAZINES OF MY ROCKET PISTOLS WERE EMPTY.

©JOHN DILLE CO

I DROPPED MY GUNS AND SPRANG FOR THE MONGOL, WHO TURNED ON ME LIKE A WILD BEAST AT BAY.

LT DICK CALKINS AIR CORPS RES 107

(TO BE CONTINUED)

I HAD INDEED EXPECTED A FIGHT TO THE DEATH BUT—

I GIVE UP!

WISE LAD.

THIS SURELY WINDS UP THE WORK OF THE GOLDEN DRAGONS

WHAM!

WILMA LANDED WITH OUR ROCKET SHIP AT MY SIGNAL, AND DESTROYED THE GREAT PROJECTOR.

BUT IT WAS WICKED TO FOMENT WAR AGAINST THE EMPEROR AND ORGZONES.

THE WORK OF A LIFETIME—

WE TOOK OM-KA-ZORIL BACK TO HIS LABORATORY, WHERE

I REALIZE IT NOW. OUR HUNGER FOR FREEDOM MADE US PLAN IT. LISTEN—I'VE AN IDEA!

WHAT IS IT?

JICK CALKINS 108

TO BE CONT'D.

WHAT'S YOUR BIG IDEA OM-KA-ZORIL

THE GOLDEN DRAGONS PLOTTED TO EMBROIL THE EMPEROR IN WAR WITH YOUR ORGZONES. YOU HAVE SMASHED OUR PLAN. I AM AT YOUR MERCY

ZONE OF FEDERATION

ZONE OF MONGOL DOMINATION

PROTECTIVE INFLUENCE

BUT YOUR FEDERATION WOULD LIKE TO SEE THE EMPEROR KEPT TOO BUSY WITH HIS OWN TROUBLES TO RAID AND PERSECUTE THE NORTH AMERICAN ORGS. WHY NOT LET THE GOLDEN DRAGONS WORK WITH YOU?

WE HAVE NO AUTHORITY TO BIND THE FEDERATION TO SUCH AN AGREEMENT

BUT SUPPOSE I MAKE YOU TWO THE SUPREME HEADS OF THE SOCIETY

(TO BE CONTINUED)

HOW DO WE KNOW THAT YOU REALLY HAVE THIS VAST SPY SYSTEM YOU CLAIM?

LOOK IN THE TELEVISION — I'LL SHOW YOU

OM-KA-ZORIL HAD JUST OFFERED WILMA AND ME THE LEADERSHIP OF THE GOLDEN DRAGONS, THE MONGOL REVOLUTIONARY SOCIETY

THE VICEROY OF CHICAGO! LITTLE DOES HE DREAM THAT HIS EVERY ACT IS VISIBLE IN THE DETECTO-TELEVISION OF THE GOLDEN DRAGONS

AT THIS MOMENT OUR MEN AS YOU SEE, ARE RAIDING A DISINTEGRATOR WAREHOUSE IN THE IMPERIAL CITY

EVEN THE EMPEROR HIMSELF —

NOW TO STRIKE THEM DOWN

(TO BE CONTINUED) 110

NO — LET THEM LIVE. I WILL USE THEM TO MY ADVANTAGE

SOME SYSTEM THESE MONGOLS HAVE.

WILMA AND I REALIZED THAT CONTROL OF THE GOLDEN DRAGONS MEANT VAST POWER

THE FATE OF NORTH AMERICA TREMBLES IN YOUR HANDS

YOU SAID IT, OM. BUT WE DON'T DARE RADIOPHONE, WE'D BE OVERHEARD

AT WILMA'S SUGGESTION, I STREAKED THROUGH THE NIGHT FOR NIAGARA TO SEE MacGREGOR.

ONE FALSE MOVE, MY SAFFRON FRIEND, AND YOU GO BOOM!

WHILE WILMA GUARDED THE WILY MONGOL.

(TO BE CONTINUED) 111

— BUT COULDN'T WE LOCK OM-KA-ZORIL UP HERE IN NIAGARA, SIR?

IMPOSSIBLE! TOO RISKY. GET YOUR SHIP — I HAE A PLAN

I REACHED G.H.Q IN THE GRAY DAWN AND ROUSED MacGREGOR

WE MADE A QUICK FLIGHT AND LANDED —

YON'S THE DESAIRTED FORT OF THE ELMIRA ORGZONE. YE CAN HAE IT FOR A PRISON. I'LL SEND YE A SQUAD

I'LL GET THE PRISONER AT ONCE

OH WILMA! BRING HIM OUT!

REACHING THE SPOT WHERE I'D LEFT WILMA, I ANCHORED MY ROCKET SHIP AND JUMPED FOR OM'S LABORATORY

SHE'S GONE! WHAT'S THIS? GAS! AND I LEFT HER WITH THAT MONGOL WIZARD!

TO BE CONTINUED

MEETING THE MONGOLS

MEETING THE MONGOLS

TENSED FOR ACTION, I DROPPED DOWN INTO THE THE TUNNEL LEADING TO THE SECRET LAIR OF THE GOLDEN DRAGONS

IS THIS A TRAP? WELL HERE GOES ANYHOW

DID YOU GENTLEMEN WISH TO SEE ME?

IT WAS ALL A MISTAKE! I DID NOT WISH TO BE RESCUED BUCK ROGERS. WE DRAGONS DO NOT BREAK FAITH.

LEAVING ONE OF THEIR SUBORDINATES IN CHARGE OF THE LAIR AT DAVENPORT, OM KA-ZORIL AND MORKE KA-LONO WERE SOON INSTALLED IN THE ELMIRA ORGZONE, WITH THE APPARATUS.

(TO BE CONTINUED)

BUCK! AN AIR FORCE IS APPROACHING!

AUTOMATIC AIR SENTRY — ALTITUDE INDICATOR — DIRECTION INDICATOR — SPEED INDICATOR

BRR-RING BRR-BR-BR

MONGOL OR AMERICAN?

121

LIEUTENANT BLAIR REPORTS TO CAPTAIN ROGERS FOR DUTY

O.K. YOU'RE TO GUARD OUR PRISONERS HERE

YOU'LL REMAIN IN RADIO COMMAND OF THE GOLDEN DRAGON'S SPY SYSTEM

BUT WILL OPERATE SOLELY UNDER YOUR ORDERS

IN THE NEXT FEW DAYS WILMA AND I LEARNED MUCH OF THE GOLDEN DRAGON'S SECRETS.

Buck and Wilma Come to me at once — Grave crisis! MacGregor

THEN CAME A MESSAGE THROUGH THE RADIO WRITER.

(TO BE CONTINUED)

122.

KEEP A SHARP WATCH ON THOSE TWO MONGOLS, BLAIR I DON'T FULLY TRUST THEM AND LOOK ALIVE FOR ANY INSTRUCTIONS WE MAY SEND FROM NIAGARA

YES. SIR

MACGREGOR SAID, "GRAVE CRISIS" WHAT CAN IT BE, WILMA?

SOUNDS LIKE WAR-OR SPIES IN THE CAPITAL

WE ROCKETED FULL BLAST FOR NIAGARA.

HERE WE ARE· HEADQUARTERS BUILDING

WE BURNT THE AIR GETTING HERE

WHAT'S THE "GRAVE CRISIS," MAC?

GRAVE ENOUGH! THE CITY'S FU' O' SPIES AND ASSASSINS· NO MON'S LIFE IS SAFE· YE MAUN HELP US

123

(TO BE CONTINUED)

A GENERAL KILLED! A COLONEL MISSING! TREATY WITH NAVAJO ORGZONE GONE· AND TODAY TH' PLANS FOR TH' NEW SUPER-ROCKET GUNS HAE VANISHED

OH, HOW TERRIBLE!

WHAT MEASURES HAVE YOU TAKEN?

WE HAE SURROUNDED TH' CITY WI' A CORDON O' ROCKET SHIPS AN' GROUND GUARDS· NO MON CAN PASS OOT!

AND WE'RE TO COMB THE CITY FOR SPIES?

I HAE PASSED THE WOR-RRD THAT ANY ORDER YE GIVE IS TAE BE OBSAIRVED

LET'S GO!

GENERAL MACGREGOR

JUMP! A KNIFE!

WHIZZZZZZZAP!

GENERAL MACGREGOR

124

TO BE CONTINUED

31

MEETING THE MONGOLS

35

THAT LOOKS LIKE HIM!

WE SCATTERED TO HUNT FOR KILLER KANE. I ROUNDED THE CORNER AND SAW A LEAPING FIGURE IN THE DISTANCE.

IT IS KILLER KANE! MAYBE I WON'T TAKE THAT GUY APART!

IN ONE MORE LEAP I WOULD HAVE BEEN ON HIM, BUT--

WOWEE! WHAT A SMELL!

TRY THIS PERFUME ON YOUR HANDKERCHIEF, ROGERS!

BAM!

© JOHN DILLE CO.

WHY - WHAT! HE'S DISAPPEARED!

141

(TO BE CONTINUED)

KANE'S SMOKE BOMB PARALYZED MY SENSES LONG ENOUGH FOR HIM TO GET AWAY.

I TOOK A SUBWAY TO WILMA'S QUARTERS FEELING VERY BLUE —

BUCK DEAR, WHY NOT RADIOPHONE OM? IF WONG IS A GOLDEN DRAGON, HE'LL BE IN TOUCH WITH HIM

YEAH, I MIGHT TRACE KANE THAT WAY. NOW, HOW DOES THAT SECRET PHONE CODE GO

I'LL GO AND GET DRESSED

HELLO- H-E-L-L-O, OM? 24- 32-78-85-27-89-54- WHAT TH'- - - , WHAT'S THE MATTER WITH THIS RADIO?

A DEAFENING ROAR OF STATIC CUT ME OFF·····

© JOHN DILLE CO.

WHAT'S THE BIG IDEA?

WE'RE JUST PINCHING YOU BOTH AS SPIES, THASSALL!

YOU'RE ALL WET, CORPORAL, I'M CAPTAIN ROGERS.

NOW, I'LL TELL ONE

142

(TO BE CONTINUED)

WHAT MADE YOU THINK WE WERE SPIES, CORPORAL?

WE GOT RADIO- PHONE ORDERS TO PINCH ANYONE IN THIS APARTMENT. IT WAS LIKE THIS, SIR

MP

WILMA AND I QUICKLY CLEARED OURSELVES OF SUSPICION AS MONGOL SPIES ---

HELLO-HELLO, OM? - 24- 32-78- 85-27- 89 54- 2

OPERATOR ON CHANNELL 757 REPORTING ATTEMPTED CODE MESSAGE FROM LOCATION R-K- 483, LEVEL 15 - WHICH I AM KILLING WITH STATIC

RADIO CENSORSHIP BUREAU

JOHN DILLE CO.

CLANG—CLANG! ROCKET CAR ATTENTION! RADIO CENSOR REPORTS SPIES TRYING TO RADIO FROM R-K-483, 15TH FLOOR GO THERE AT ONCE!

C'MON, WE'LL MAKE A PINCH

MILITARY POLICE 5TH ZONE

AND SO THAT'S HOW IT HAPPENED, SIR

SH-H-H SOMEBODY'S COMING—IT'S KILLER KANE AND LANLU!

MP

143

TO BE CONT'D

I'M SCARED, BUCK! KILLER KANE IS SO TRICKY!

SLAM HIM WHEN HE COMES IN!

LEAVE IT TO US, SIR.

© JOHN DILLE CO.

OH! IT'S LANLU!

E-E-YAH!

LOOK OUT! YOU FELLOWS, HE'LL GET AWAY

HA! A TRAP

OH, WHAT A SMELL!

HE GOT AWAY WITH IT AGAIN!

I'LL CALL AGAIN, WILMA, WHEN YOU HAVE NO COMPANY!

WHY, KILLER KANE'S GONE

WHEN I LAY MY HANDS ON THAT TRAITOR, I'LL -- I'LL —

TO BE CONT'D

144

MEETING THE MONGOLS

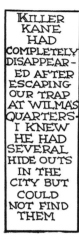

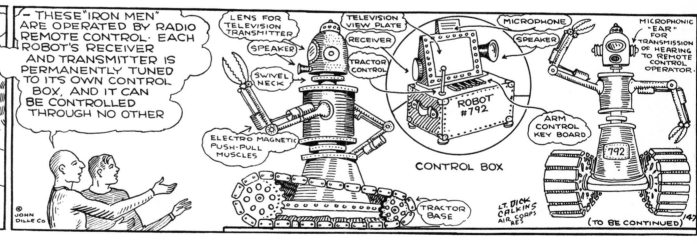

2
CAPTURING THE MONGOL EMPEROR

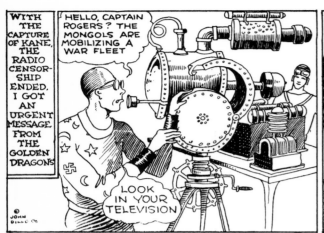

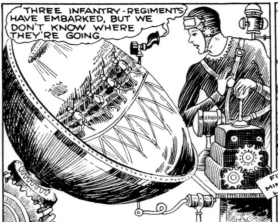

CAPTURING THE MONGOL EMPEROR

THE MONGOL SHIPS DROPPED LIKE STONES. THE TELEV-EYE FOLLOWED RELENTLESSLY.

GET THOSE DISINTEGRATORS WORKING!

M-M-101, R-63--

BUT THE MONGOL GUNNERS COULD NOT TOUCH THE LITTLE TELEV-EYE WITH THEIR ANNIHILATING BEAMS.

HELP! HELP!

SUDDENLY IT BORE DOWN ON THE MONARCH AGAIN.

OH DRAGONS OF DOOM! THE EARTH IS FOUR MILES BELOW!

H-E-L-P! HELP!

LT. DICK CALKINS AIR CORPS RES.

(TO BE CONTINUED) 160.

THE TELEV-EYE IS CALLING!

AT THE CONTROL BOARD WE SAW THE TELEVISION SCREEN SUDDENLY BECOME A WHIRLING CHAOS.

?? ??

WE DIDN'T GUESS WHAT HAD HAPPENED UNTIL THE FALLING MONARCH'S ------

GREAT GUNS!

IT'S THE EMPEROR!

HE'LL BE KILLED!

-- FACE APPEARED ON THE SCREEN

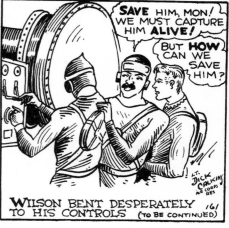

SAVE HIM, MON! WE MUST CAPTURE HIM ALIVE!

BUT HOW CAN WE SAVE HIM?

WILSON BENT DESPERATELY TO HIS CONTROLS (TO BE CONTINUED) 161

THE TELEV-EYE, HAVING A ZERO WEIGHT BALANCE, COULD NO MORE ACT AS AN ANTI-GRAVITY DEVICE THAN A FEATHER. BUT AT 500 FEET WILSON SUCCEEDED IN NOSING IT UP UNDER ROCKET POWER, BY RADIO CONTROL.

BY CLEVER MANIPULATION, HE BALANCED IT SO, CHECKING THE FALL BY A DOWN-BLAST.

AND GENTLY THE MONGOL MONARCH--

--DROPPED INTO THE GULF OF CALIFORNIA.

JICK CALKINS 162

TO BE CONTINUED

AS THE MONGOL MONARCH PLUNGED INTO THE GULF OF CALIFORNIA OUR TELEV-EYE WENT DEAD SHORT CIRCUITED BY THE WATER.

BUCK, MON, GO OOT AND BRING ME BACK THAT EMPEROR OR PROOF HE'S DEAD.

I'LL TAKE THREE ROCKET SHIPS

I TELL YOU IT'S DANGEROUS, NO WORK FOR A GIRL!

APPLE SAUCE! I'M AS GOOD A SOLDIER AS YOU ARE

WILMA WAS ANGRY BECAUSE I WOULDN'T TAKE HER WITH ME.

ALL READY, SIR.

WON'T YOU EVEN SAY GOOD BYE, WILMA?

NO!

HE N-N-NEVER SAID G-G-G-GOOD BYE!

WHAT DO I CARE IF SHE DIDN'T SAY GOOD BYE!

TO BE CONT'D

LT. DICK CALKINS AIR CORPS RES.

163.

CAPTURING THE MONGOL EMPEROR

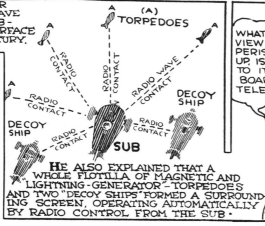

AFTER SEEING THE WAY YOU CHUCK LIGHTNING AROUND, I CAN SEE AIRSHIDS AREN'T ALWAYS SUPREME

AIRCRAFT CAN'T CONCEAL THEMSELVES LIKE SUBS. WE CHILIANS USE FEW OF THEM FOR FIGHTING

I WONDER WHERE THEY'RE TAKING ME AND WHEN WE'LL GET THERE

BACK IN MY STATEROOM, I HAD LOTS OF TIME FOR REFLECTION—

TRAPPED!! GAS KNOCKING ME OUT, TOO... GETTING SLEEPY..... GUESS I'M DONE FOR...GOOD BYE ALL— MOTHER.

—I REMEMBERED HOW, IN 1929, I HAD BEGUN MY 500 YEARS OF SUSPENDED ANIMATION—

—WHILE THE RED MONGOLS CONQUERED AMERICA WITH THEIR GIANT AIRSHIPS, AND TERRIBLE DISINTEGRATOR RAYS. (TO BE CONTINUED) 172

HELD A PRISONER IN THE CHILIAN SUB I RECALLED HOW—

"ON THE RUINS OF NEW YORK, SAN FRANCISCO, DETROIT, AND A DOZEN OTHERS THE MONGOLS REARED CITIES OF SUPER SCIENTIFIC MAGNIFICENCE

THERE THEY SYNTHETICALLY PRODUCED MARVELOUS FOODS, TEXTILES, METALS AND AMAZING LUXURIES LEAVING TOWN ONLY FOR THE SPORT OF HUNTING WILD AMERICANS IN THE FORESTS"

—AND INDEED FOR SEVERAL GENERATIONS THE AMERICANS DID LIVE HUNTED LIVES IN THE FORESTS THAT GREW UP OVER THE ONCE CULTIVATED FARMS AND RUINED TOWNS AND CITIES. STILL THEY CHERISHED THE UNDYING FLAME OF FREEDOM, AND LITTLE BY LITTLE—

THE WIDELY SCATTERED AND LOOSELY BOUND ORGANIZATIONS OR "ORGS" BEGAN THE SLOW PROCESS OF REBUILDING A CIVILIZATION AND RECAPTURING LOST SCIENCE,

YOU'RE EITHER CRAZY, OR-A SPY! IF THAT CAVE EVER WAS A MINE IT WAS BEFORE THE DESTRUCTION OF ANCIENT PITTSBURGH IN 2029 A.D.—400 YEARS AGO!

WHOA-A-A! BACK UP! DO YOU MEAN THIS IS THE YEAR 2429?

THEN CAME MY REAWAKENING---AND WILMA

I KNEW YOU WOULD FIND ME BUCK

WILMA! DID THEY HURT YOU, LITTLE GIRL?

I THRILLED AT THE MEMORY OF HOW I HAD RESCUED WILMA FROM THE MONGOLS, AND—

WE'LL GO DIRECTLY TAE TH' AIRGUARD BUILDING

SOME VILLAGE! IT'S A WONDER THE MONGOL REDS DON'T MOP IT UP

HOW WE HAD COME TO NIAGARA, THE ONLY CITY IN AMERICA STRONG ENOUGH YET TO DEFY THE RED MONGOLS

HO HUM, IT'S A FUNNY LIFE. I WONDER WHAT WILMA'S DOING BACK IN NIAGARA

NOW, IN MY SEARCH FOR THE MONGOL EMPEROR, WHO HAD BEEN KNOCKED OVERBOARD, I HAD BEEN CAPTURED BY A CHILIAN SUBMARINE

WILMA, DEAR, SAY YOU CARE JUST A LITTLE BIT

SH! HERE'S A MESSENGER

QUICK! THE GENERAL WANTS YOU INSTANTLY!

I DID NOT KNOW HOW FRIENDLY WILMA HAD BECOME WITH TOMMY JOHNSON WHILE I WAS AWAY.

IS BUCK IN DANGER?

AYE, LASS. A PREESONER ON A CHILIAN SUBMARINE! WE'LL RESCUE HIM IN YON NEW ROCKET CRUISER!

MACGREGOR, HAVING RECEIVED JAKE'S RADIOPHONE MESSAGE WHEN THE CHILIANS CAPTURED US, SENT AT ONCE FOR WILMA—

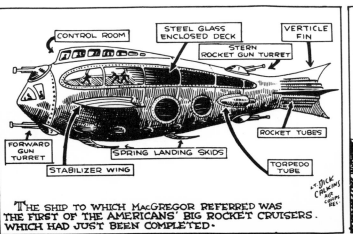

CONTROL ROOM

STEEL GLASS ENCLOSED DECK

STERN ROCKET GUN TURRET

VERTICLE FIN

FORWARD GUN TURRET

STABILIZER WING

SPRING LANDING SKIDS

ROCKET TUBES

TORPEDO TUBE

THE SHIP TO WHICH MacGREGOR REFERRED WAS THE FIRST OF THE AMERICANS' BIG ROCKET CRUISERS, WHICH HAD JUST BEEN COMPLETED.

BUT THE SHIP HAD TO BE CONDITIONED AND EQUIPPED AND IN THE MEANTIME—

FULL SPEED ASTERN!

GREAT SCOTT! WHAT'S THAT?

THE SUBMARINE APPROACHED THE CHILIAN COAST AT HIGH SPEED—
(TO BE CONTINUED) 175

46

CAPTURING THE MONGOL EMPEROR

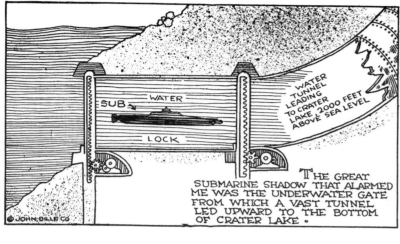

THE MONGOLS THINK THE EMPEROR WAS DROWNED. BUT THEY BLAME THE CHILIANS, NOT US! AIR MARSHALL KA-FLUI IS LEADING A FLEET HERE TO PUNISH THE CHILIANS. HE THINKS IT WILL MAKE HIM POPULAR. THEN HE'LL GRAB THE THRONE.

I GET YOU, SIR!

AS SOON AS I BOARDED THE ROCKET CRUISER, MacGREGOR TOOK ME TO HIS CABIN.

WILMA'S TO WARN THE CHILIANS, GRAB THE PREESONER AND DUCK OOT O' DANGER WI' HIM. WE HELP STAND OFF THE MONGOL AIR FLEET

GOOD! I MIGHT AS WELL BE DISINTEGRATED AS THE WAY I AM

MEANWHILE, TOMMY AND WILMA WENT TO RELEASE THE EMPEROR

(COPYRIGHT JOHN DILLE CO)

ARE YOU SURE YOU HAVE THE ORDER FOR THE PRISONER, WILMA?

RIGHT HERE, TOMMY

BUT-BUT I HAVE AN ORDER!

BUT, I TELL YOU HE LEFT FOUR DAYS AGO ON A SIGNED ORDER

SACRE! A FORGERY

(TO BE CONTINUED)

DICK CALKINS 188

WILMA HAD RADIOPHONED MacGREGOR THAT THE EMPEROR HAD SLIPPED OUT OF THE CHILIANS HANDS ON A FORGED ORDER

THAT'S WHAT COMES OF GIVING AN IMPORTANT MISSION TO A GIRL

YE'RE DAFT! SHE COULDNA' HELP IT

THAT VERY AFTERNOON OUR ROCKET CRUISER, SIGHTED THE VANGUARD OF THE MONGOL FLEET FAR BELOW US, FLYING IN THEIR INVERTED "V" FORMATION. (COPYRIGHT JOHN DILLE CO)

WE HUNG ON THEIR TAILS AS THEY PLUNGED LIKE STONES TO BRING THE CHILIAN CITY, MILES BELOW, WITHIN RANGE OF THEIR TERRIBLE DISINTEGRATOR BEAMS (TO BE CONTINUED) 189

LT. DICK CALKINS ACR

LOOK, BUCK! SEE THE DISINTEGRATOR BEAMS FLASH DOWN

ARE THE CHILIAN BATTERIES ASLEEP?

BUT THE CHILIANS WERE READY. AS THE MONGOLS' RAYS SLICED GASHES OF NOTHINGNESS ACROSS THE CITY, PALE GREEN FLASHES SHOT BACK AT THEM (COPYRIGHT JOHN DILLE CO)

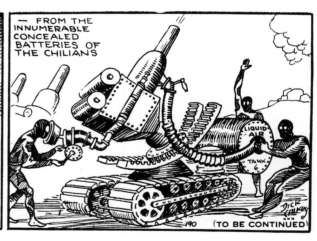

— FROM THE INNUMERABLE CONCEALED BATTERIES OF THE CHILIANS

DICK CALKINS 190 (TO BE CONTINUED)

CHILIAN AERIAL "SMUDGERS" WOVE A DENSE SMOKE SCREEN, LIKE A PROTECTING CANOPY OVER THE CITY, AND UP THROUGH THIS TORE THE STORM OF ROCKET SHRAPNEL FROM THEIR LIQUID-AIR GUNS (COPYRIGHT JOHN DILLE CO)

WE CAN'T SEE TO TRAIN OUR DISINTEGRATOR BEAMS ON THEM, CELESTIAL MONARCH

THEN DUMP THE GAS ON THEM!

ON THE BRIDGE OF AIR-MARSHAL KA-FLUI'S FLAGSHIP —

AND FROM EVERY MONGOL SHIP GREAT GAS BOMBS PLUNGED TOWARD THE SEA OF SMOKE AND THE CITY THAT LAY BENEATH IT

LT. DICK CALKINS ACR 191 (TO BE CONTINUED)

BUCK ROGERS IN THE 25th CENTURY

OH! OH! OOOOH!

JUMPING JUPITER!

THE CHILIAN "ATTRACTORS" PULLED MONSTER LIGHTNING BOLTS FROM THE SKY THROUGH THE MONGOL FLEET DESPITE THE DISTANCE WILMA AND TOMMY WERE KNOCKED OUT. (COPYRIGHT JOHN DILLE CO.)

HOOTS! 'TIS TH' END O'TH' WOR-R-R-LD

NO! IT'S CHILIAN LIGHTNING ATTRACTORS.

MACGREGOR AND I WERE NEARLY HURLED FROM THE BRIDGE OF THE ROCKET CRUISER

IT WAS THE END OF THE MONGOL SHIPS ANYHOW.

SHOOT A TELEV-EYE BELOW YON SMOKE SCREEN.

BUT HOW HAD THE CHILIAN CITY FARED? (TO BE CONTINUED)

OUR TELEV-EYE CRUISED LOW UNDER OUR RADIO CONTROL, AUTOMATICALLY BROADCASTING TO US THE VIEW OF THE WRECKED MONGOL SHIPS

WE'LL VEESIT THE ADMEERAL AND CONGRATULATE HIM.

AND TRY TO FIND WILMA

THE AIR TUBE AND STAIRWAY WRECKED, WILMA AND TOMMY WERE LEFT STRANDED HIGH ON THE CLIFF STATION (COPYRIGHT JOHN DILLE CO.)

HOW CAN WE GET DOWN, WILMA? OUR WEIGHT BALANCE IS TOO GREAT FOR THAT DISTANCE. WE'D ACCELERATE TOO FAST.

LISTEN TOMMY, I HAVE A PLAN!

TO BE CONTINUED

SEE, OUR BLOUSES WILL MAKE BIG ENOUGH PARACHUTES TO EASE US DOWN WITH THE AID OF OUR JUMPING BELTS

WILMA, YOU'RE ONE CLEVER GIRL

AM I LOCO? THEY SHOULD FALL, BUT THEY FLOAT! OH THEY'RE COMING HERE! WE ARE UNDONE.

QUICK, BELOVED, HIDE! BEFORE THEY FIND YOU!

WHAT'S THE MATTER WITH HER?

SHE'S HIDING SOMEONE FROM US.

CATCH ME! I'M FAINTING

QUICK TOMMY! I BET IT'S THE MONGOL EMPEROR

WHAT THE—?

TO BE CONTINUED

OH STOP! WAIT!

WHAT'S THIS, A FAKE FAINT?

WHAT FOR? LET GO!

THE CHILIAN GIRL DELAYED WILMA AND TOMMY AS THEY TRIED TO LEAP AFTER THE FLEEING MONGOL

AH, LET HIM GO HE'S REACHED THE VILLAGE NOW ANYHOW. YOU CAN'T CATCH HIM!

WELL, IN THAT CASE—

OH PUT YOUR SHIRT ON, TOM. THE SHOW'S OVER

(COPYRIGHT JOHN DILLE CO.)

I THINK WE'VE LOCATED THE MONGOL EMPEROR. BRING THE ROCKET CRUISER AT ONCE!

WILMA RADIOPHONED MACGREGOR AT ONCE

WHAT'LL WE DO?

TAK' TH' ROCKET CRUISER AND ARREST THAT MONGOL. I'LL GET A WARRANT FRAE THE ADMEERAL

MACGREGOR AND I HAD NO SOONER LANDED FROM THE ROCKET CRUISER THAN HE GOT WILMA'S MESSAGE (TO BE CONTINUED)

52

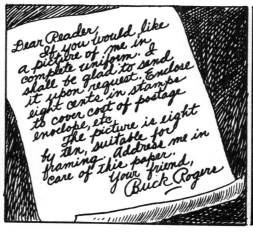

Like chain shot in the days of ancient frigates, the heavy weights spread wide apart. But the net and the steel cable were deweighted with inerton.

(COPYRIGHT JOHN DILLE CO.)

"Sacre! Our lifting fans are crushed! We fall!"

Hopelessly entangled, the gyro swung like a pendulum at the end of the cable as we reeled it in.

"He's not the Mongol emperor!" "Buck Rogers! My old friend!" "Morke ka lona! But where is the Mongol emperor?"

(TO BE CONTINUED)

We thought we had nabbed the Mongol emperor, but our captive turned out to be Morke ka lono, one of the heads of the secret Mongol order of Golden Dragons.

"Why are you here, Morke, instead of in the Elmira headquarters of the Golden Dragons, in Lt. Blair's custody?" "Well, it was like this—"

"Now! Everything shown on this screen will be broadcast to Morke. One of our spies sneaked into your intelligence office and 'tapped' your televisor—"

"Ha! I must capture him before Buck Rogers does!" "So I also saw the emperor plunge into the Gulf of California—"

(COPYRIGHT JOHN DILLE CO.)

"It's the emperor!" "The Chilians have him! I'll follow!" "I eluded your guard and streaked for the gulf—"

(TO BE CONTINUED)

Morke ka lono continued his story, telling us

"You have beautiful eyes!" "You say such sweet things.—Of course I will help you!" "I landed at the villa of Senorita Adala, who fell hard for me ...."

"Out! Traitor! I am your emperor!" "Oof!" "With her aid and her brother's, I freed the emperor from the asylum, but when I got him to the ship—" He escapes.

"So he got away with my ship. Then you came." "You broke our agreement. It's your fault!" "Pipe down, Wilma—the main idea is to catch the emperor."

"One side, folks, one side or a le' off! A radiogram, sir! The Mongol cities are seething with intrigue." "Quick, man—the details!!!"

(COPYRIGHT JOHN DILLE CO.)

(TO BE CONTINUED)

The radiogram from Niagara informed us that the Mongol viceroy of Chicago had proclaimed himself emperor.

"The die is cast! We shall consolidate our reign at once." "Huzzah! Huzzah! Vivalo!"

In the imperial city the Golden Dragons had proclaimed a republic—

"Hail, loyal subjects!" The emperor himself landed at Omaha—

In view of this ominous news, we rocketed full blast for home. A crisis was brewing!

(COPYRIGHT JOHN DILLE CO.)

(TO BE CONTINUED)

54

CAPTURING THE MONGOL EMPEROR

CAPTURING THE MONGOL EMPEROR

CAPTURING THE MONGOL EMPEROR

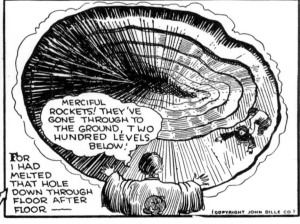

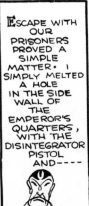

CAPTURING THE MONGOL EMPEROR

3

MARTIANS INVADE EARTH
BATTLE ON THE MOON

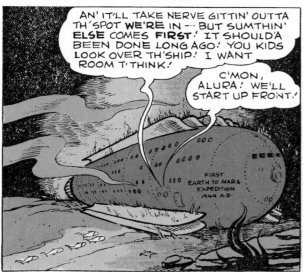

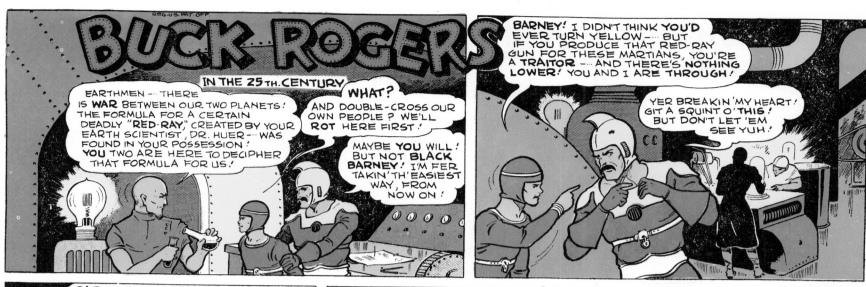

BUCK ROGERS IN THE 25th CENTURY

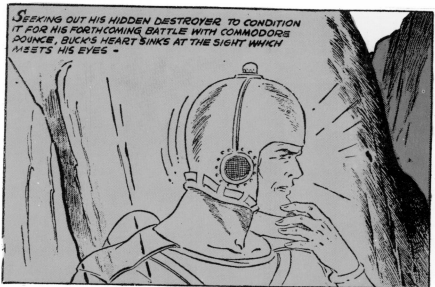

SEEKING OUT HIS HIDDEN DESTROYER TO CONDITION IT FOR HIS FORTHCOMING BATTLE WITH COMMODORE POUNCE, BUCK'S HEART SINKS AT THE SIGHT WHICH MEETS HIS EYES—

—FOR THE SHIP ON WHICH BUCK'S LIFE DEPENDS, IS NOW A SHATTERED HULK!

MY DESTROYER! A TOTAL WRECK! IT'S.....HARD TO BELIEVE! I'D LIKE TO LAY HANDS ON THE GUY WHO DID THIS!

BUT THAT'S THE MYSTERY! WHO?? DUAL...NAMTAC...BENGAL....NONE OF THEM KNEW WHERE MY DESTROYER WAS HIDDEN.....AND THEY WERE TOO BUSY HUNTING FOR ME, TO BOTHER SEARCHING FOR MY SHIP!

AND YET...SOMEONE DID THE JOB.....

OH·OH! THERE'S THE ANSWER! THAT BIG FOOTPRINT TELLS THE STORY!

MEANWHILE · ON MARS ·

HERE COMES THE FINAL DIVE, SABRE! THE MASTER WILL NEED THE POWER OF SATAN HIMSELF, TO CLEAR THE HOOP THIS TIME!

YES, KLAWW! HIS SHIP HAS BUT ONE INCH CLEARANCE ALL AROUND! I...I JUST HOPE...

BUT SABRE'S HOPES ARE FUTILE! AGAIN, WITH UNCANNY SKILL, POUNCE DRIVES HIS OCTO-JET ROARING THROUGH THE HOOP—

ALERT, BELOW! I'M LANDING! LINE UP THE CAPTIVE PILOTS!

ATTENTION! I MUST SHARPEN MY AIM FOR A FELLOW NAMED ROGERS...SO THIS WILL BE YOUR LAST FLIGHT! YOUR SHIPS ARE UNARMED, SO YOU MUST DEPEND ON FLYING SKILL TO STAY ALIVE! AS I DESTROY THE FIRST MAN, THE SECOND WILL TAKE OFF—AND SO ON! THAT IS ALL!

SIR, WE BEG A LAST FAVOR! WE'VE WRITTEN LETTERS HOME...TO OUR FAMILIES...TO SAY GOODBYE! WE ONLY ASK THAT YOU....

HOW DARE YOU WASTE MY TIME WITH STUPID REQUESTS?

SABRE, NOTIFY THE FAMILIES OF THESE "GUINEA PIGS" THAT THEIR SONS WERE COWARDS AND DIED IN DISGRACE!

PILOT NO. 1.....BOARD YOUR SHIP!

AND—BACK ON THE MOON—

....SO THAT'S THE STORY, DOC! WHEN BENGAL'S BIG MUSCLE-MAN, "STRANGLER", TRIED TO MURDER MISS FORTUNE, I BEAT HIM TO A PULP..THEN LET HIM GO!

SO WHEN "STRANGLER" CHANCED TO FIND MY SHIP, HE BLEW IT UP! BUT HIS ACT OF REVENGE BACK-FIRED! HERE'S WHAT'S LEFT OF HIM!

COPYRIGHT 1947 JOHN F. DILLE CO.

BUT---BUCK! NOW WHAT? FLYING THIS BANGED-UP SHIP OF DOC'S, YOUR CHANCES AGAINST POUNCE ARE ONE IN A MILLION!

THREE IN A MILLION, BARNEY—WITH YOU AND DOC ON MY TEAM! COME ON! LET'S GET BUSY! THAT LITTLE WAIF IS GOING TO GET HER FACE LIFTED—AND BECOME A FIGHTING LADY!!

307 TO BE CONTINUED

BUCK ROGERS IN THE 25th CENTURY

BATTLE ON THE MOON

BUCK! I'VE GUESSED YER SECRET ---- TH' REASON FER THIS EXTRA COCKPIT!! WHEN Y' FIGHT COMMODORE POUNCE, YER TAKIN' **ME** ALONG --- AS GUNNER!! SWELL!!

GUESS AGAIN, BARNEY! AS MUCH AS I'D LIKE YOU WITH ME, MY FIGHT WITH POUNCE WILL BE A PERSONAL DUEL ---

... AND HAVING A GUNNER WOULD BE A BREACH OF "COMBAT ETIQUETTE"!

I GUESS YER RIGHT, BUCK --- BUT, DOGGONIT, IT DON'T MAKE SENSE! A GUY FLYIN' SOLO, CAN'T USE TWO COCKPITS!

HEH! GREAT JOKERS, THOSE TWO, MISS FORTUNE! BARNEY HAS A SECRET "SOMETHING" THAT'LL HELP BUCK DEFEAT COMMODORE POUNCE --- BUT HE WON'T TELL BUCK WHAT IT IS! LIKES TO KEEP HIM GUESSING!

YES! BUT BUCK HAS TURNED THE TABLES, DR. HUER ----

---HE'S GOT BARNEY IN A 'DITHER, WONDERING WHO'S GOING TO OCCUPY THAT MYSTERIOUS EXTRA COCKPIT!

HEH! TWO COCKPITS FOR ONE FIGHTER! I CAN'T FIGURE THAT ONE OUT, EITHER! BUCK'S GOT SOMETHING UP HIS SLEEVE!

MEANWHILE - ON MARS - COMMODORE POUNCE, MASTER OF ROCKET-COMBAT, CONTINUES HIS CRUEL PRACTICE-TRIALS.

AH! N⁰ 4, EH? THE SIX-FOOTER WHO CALLED ME A "SAWED-OFF LITTLE RUNT"! WELL, INSULTING ONE, THERE'S SOMETHING AWAITING YOU ON THE GROUND, THAT IS EVEN SHORTER THAN I AM ----

BUT IT WILL BE **MORE** THAN AMPLE TO CONTAIN WHAT'S LEFT OF YOUR HAUGHTY FRAME WHEN **I'M** FINISHED WITH YOU!

FIRST ---- THE MAGNETIC-RAY --- TO HOLD YOU IN POSITION!!

HA HA HA HA --- I'VE **GOT** YOU!

AND NOW, N⁰ 4 ---- WE'LL SEE IF THIS ACID-HEAT-RAY CAN ROAST OUT SOME OF YOUR ARROGANCE, EH ?? THEN I'VE GOT SOME **REAL** TERRORS PLANNED FOR YOU!

AH! ARE YOU READ·D·D·Y·Y ?

LOOK! I CAN'T STAND THIS ANY LONGER! POUNCE IS GOING TO TURN THAT HEAT-RAY ON N⁰ 4! THAT FILTHY LITTLE WEASEL!

YES! HE'S TIRED OF MERELY KILLING! NOW HE'S TURNED TO METHODS OF SLOW TORTURE! IT'LL BE THE SAME FOR ALL OF US --- UNLESS ---

YES ---- UNLESS ---- PSST--- EDGE CLOSER TO THE GUARDS! WHEN I COUNT THREE ---- GIVE 'EM THE WORKS! SHHH--- ONE ·· TWO ·· TH···

A FEW MOMENTS LATER -

QUICK, NOW! INTO YOUR SHIPS --- AND RAM THAT MARTIAN SATAN INTO ETERNITY!

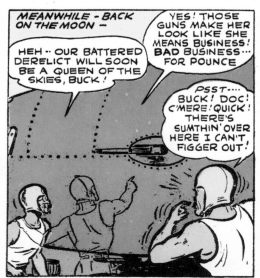

MEANWHILE - BACK ON THE MOON -

HEH -- OUR BATTERED DERELICT WILL SOON BE A QUEEN OF THE SKIES, BUCK!

YES! THOSE GUNS MAKE HER LOOK LIKE SHE MEANS BUSINESS! **BAD** BUSINESS FOR POUNCE

PSST --- BUCK! DOC! C'MERE! QUICK! THERE'S SUMTHIN' OVER HERE I CAN'T FIGGER OUT!

HEH! I WONDER WHAT **THAT** COULD MEAN ??

SEARCH ME, DOC! WHAT D' **YOU** MAKE OF IT, BUCK ?

SHH --- THE ONLY WAY WE CAN FIND OUT IS TO WAIT ---- AND **WATCH**!!

310
TO BE CONTINUED

BATTLE ON THE MOON

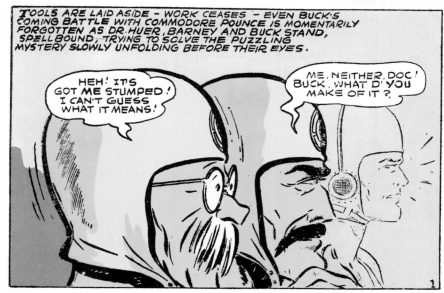

TOOLS ARE LAID ASIDE — WORK CEASES — EVEN BUCK'S COMING BATTLE WITH COMMODORE POUNCE IS MOMENTARILY FORGOTTEN AS DR. HUER, BARNEY AND BUCK STAND, SPELLBOUND, TRYING TO SOLVE THE PUZZLING MYSTERY SLOWLY UNFOLDING BEFORE THEIR EYES.

HEH! IT'S GOT ME STUMPED! I CAN'T GUESS WHAT IT MEANS!

ME, NEITHER, DOC! BUCK, WHAT D' YOU MAKE OF IT?

SO FAR, BARNEY, I'M STUMPED, TOO! BUT WE'LL KNOW MORE WHEN WE SEE THE REST OF IT! JUST BE PATIENT!

DOGGONIT, BUCK! I'VE SEEN PUZZLIN' MYSTERIES B'FORE — BUT THIS'N BEATS 'EM ALL

SHH — EDGE CLOSER! MAYBE THERE'S MORE TO IT WE CAN'T SEE — THAT'LL GIVE US A CLUE!

HEH — YES! ANYTHING TO RELIEVE THIS SUSPENSE!

PO H O-LOO

HMM — IT STILL DOESN'T MAKE SENSE!

MEANWHILE — ON MARS — IN PREPARATION FOR HIS COMING BATTLE WITH BUCK, COMMODORE POUNCE TESTS HIS VARIOUS LETHAL WEAPONS ON CAPTIVE PILOTS IN UNARMED SHIPS —

NOW, PILOT N°4 — WE'LL SEE HOW YOU LIKE THIS ACID-HEAT-RAY —

WAIT!! AN EMERGENCY CALL FROM THE FIELD! WHAT CAN THAT MEAN?

MAGNETIC RAY

— SABRE TO POUNCE — URGENT — BEWARE, MASTER — THE FOUR REMAINING TARGET-SHIP PILOTS HAVE BROKEN AWAY — AND MANNED THEIR SHIPS — THEY'RE COMING UP TO ATTACK YOU!!

ARREST THE STUPID GUARDS WHO LET THIS HAPPEN, SABRE! I CAN HANDLE THE SITUATION UP HERE!

SO! OUR HEROES COME TO SAVE THEIR PAL FROM BEING ROASTED!! EAGER TO DIE — IF YOU CAN TAKE ME TO ETERNITY WITH YOU, EH?

SIMPLE DOLTS! I SHOULD PICK YOU OFF ONE AT A TIME — BUT I HAVE A BETTER IDEA! I'LL LET YOU DESTROY YOURSELVES! AND I'LL EVEN RELEASE N°4 — TO HELP YOU!

LIKE HOUNDS CLOSING IN ON A CORNERED WOLF, THE ATTACKING SQUADRON MANEUVERS INTO POSITION FOR THE KILL — TEN EYES, BURNING WITH HATRED, WATCH POUNCE'S EVERY MOVE — BUT POUNCE ONLY LEERS BACK — AND CALMLY PRESSES A BUTTON.

ELECTRONIC MIR—

THEN — SUDDENLY —

THIS IS IT, Y' WEASEL OF SATAN! WE'RE GOING TO RAM YOU TWENTY FEET INTO THE GROUND!

SO-LONG, Y' SAWED-OFF MURDER-MONKEY! THIS IS YOUR CURTAIN TIME!

CURTAINS FOR ALL OF US, BUT IT'S WORTH IT! HAPPY LANDINGS, MEN!

COPYRIGHT 1941 JOHN F. DILLE CO.

AND — BACK ON THE MOON —

HEH! WELL — AT LEAST WE KNOW OUR SHIP'S NEW NAME HAS SOMETHING TO DO WITH COMMODORE POUNCE

YEAH! BUT I STILL DON'T GIT TH' LAST PART! IS THAT ALL THERE IS TO IT, MISS FORTUNE?

YES! BUCK'S COMING FIGHT WITH THAT LITTLE "MARTIAN NAPOLEON", POUNCE, WILL BE A SCIENTIFIC BATTLE THAT'LL MAKE HISTORY — SO I — WAIT —!! I FORGOT SOMETHIN'!

POUNCE'S H O-LOO

POUNCE'S H_2O-LOO

BATTLE ON THE MOON

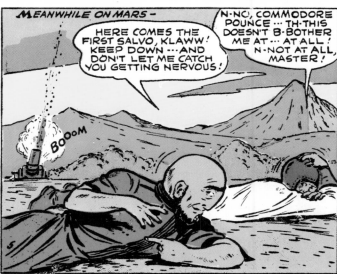

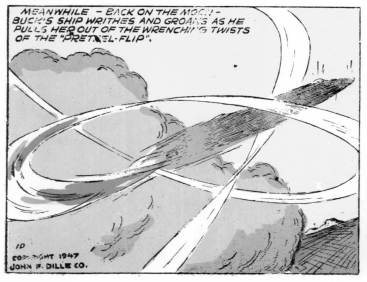

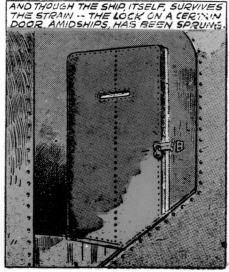

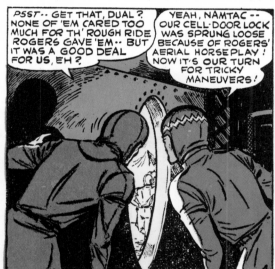

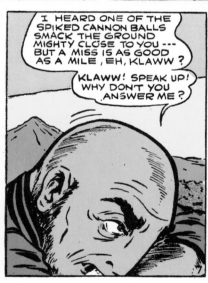

BUCK ROGERS IN THE 25th CENTURY

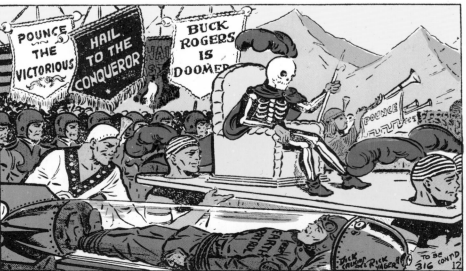

BATTLE ON THE MOON

BUCK ROGERS IN THE 25th CENTURY

LIKE A FLEETING SHADOW OF DEATH, COMMODORE POUNCE'S POWERFUL OCTO-JET FLASHES THROUGH THE VAST MARTIAN FOG-BANKS, OUTWARD BOUND - TOWARD EARTH'S MOON.

MEANWHILE - ON THE MOON -

COMIN', BUCK!

AWRIGHT, WEASELS --- FRONT AN' CENTER! Y'GOT SOME FANCY EXPLAININ' T'DO!

PSST-- REMEMBER, NAMTAC --- WHEN ROGERS STARTS ASKIN' QUESTIONS -- WE AREN'T TALKIN'!

DUAL AND NAMTAC --- IN ORDER TO GRAB THESE URANIUM FIELDS DOC HUER DISCOVERED, YOU CALLED YOUR MARTIAN PAL, POUNCE, TO COME HERE AND HELP YOU TAKE 'EM AWAY FROM US --- IF POSSIBLE!

BUT, TO BE EXTRA SURE OF SUCCESS, YOU ESCAPED THE SHIP'S BRIG AND PULLED SOME SABOTAGE THAT'D MAKE POUNCE A LEAD-PIPE CINCH TO KNOCK ME OFF, ONCE THE FIREWORKS GET UNDER WAY! VERY CLEVER!

I'D BE IN A SWEET SPOT IF POUNCE SHOWED UP NOW --- WOULDN'T I? CONTROLS FOULED, GUNS JAMMED AND HALF THE ROCKET POWER CUT OFF --- DAMAGE IT'D TAKE US A MONTH TO LOCATE ------ BUT----

---- WITH YOUR HELP WE CAN SPOT THE TROUBLE AND MAKE REPAIRS IN SHORT ORDER! OKAY --- TALK --- WHERE DO WE START?

HMM -- GUESS THEY DON'T WANTA TALK, BUCK! MEBBE IF I PLUG ONE OF 'EM IT'LL LOOSEN TH' OTHER'S TONGUE!

OH --- SO THEY WON'T TALK, EH? DUAL --- NAMTAC --- SEE THAT "EXTRA COCKPIT"? IT'S A LITTLE IDEA OF MINE THAT'S KEPT DOC, BARNEY AND MISS FORTUNE MYSTIFIED --- AS TO ITS PURPOSE!

BUT NOW'S A GOOD TIME TO REVEAL THE MYSTERIOUS SECRET!

'BOUT TIME Y'DID, BUCK!

YES! WHEN YOU FIGHT POUNCE, YOU CAN'T SIT IN TWO PLACES AT ONCE, BUCK! WHAT'S THE ANSWER?

JUST THIS! THAT COCKPIT WAS BUILT FOR THE TWO GUYS WHO HIRED POUNCE TO COME HERE! YES, DUAL AND NAMTAC --- I THOUGHT YOU MIGHT ENJOY A CLOSE-UP OF THE FIGHT YOU PROMOTED!

HUH?! YOU MEAN WE GOTTA SIT UP THERE --- WHEN YOU AN' POUNCE FIGHT IT OUT?

THAT'S THE IDEA, NAMTAC! GUNS OR NO GUNS --- FOULED CONTROLS OR NOT --- YOU TWO PUPS ARE SITTING IN ON THIS DOG-FIGHT!

DUAL! WE'LL BE ---- KILLED! BLOWN T' ATOMS! IF POUNCE WINS, IT'S THE END OF US --- AND TH' WAY WE FOULED UP ROGERS' SHIP, POUNCE CAN'T HELP WINNIN'!!

SKIP THE JABBER, NAMTAC, YOU IDIOT! TOOLS, ROGERS! GIVE US THE TOOLS AND LET'S GET BUSY! POUNCE WILL BE HERE ANY MINUTE!

COPYRIGHT 1947 JOHN F. DILLE CO.

MEANWHILE -- FLASHING ACROSS SPACE LIKE A GREASED METEOR -

HA HA HA HA HA I CAN SEE IT ALL NOW! ROGERS' SHIP IN FLAMES --- THEN ---- CHARRED WRECKAGE ON SOME NAMELESS MOON-CRATER! MY CROWNING VICTORY! HA HA HA HA HA

I'M COMING, ROGERS! I'M COMING!!

TO BE CONTINUED

112

BATTLE ON THE MOON

DOC! COME QUICK!

WHAT'S UP, BUCK?

HERE! TAKE A READ AT THIS, DOC ... IT CONCERNS A CERTAIN ... GUEST ... WE'VE BEEN EXPECTING!

...WAR SHIP...APPROACHING SPEED 2896 S.D.P.H. DIRECTION ... HEH ... A BEE-LINE FROM MARS! YES, BUCK ... IT'S COMMODORE POUNCE, ALL RIGHT!

BZZZ

DANGER

QUICK, DOC ... YOU AND MISS FORTUNE GATHER WHAT EQUIPMENT AND SUPPLIES YOU'LL NEED, WHILE I CHECK ON DUAL AND NAMTAC!

WAR SHIP APPROACHING, BARNEY ... UNIDENTIFIED, BUT THREE GUESSES WHO?!! WHAT'S THE SCORE HERE? HOW LONG BEFORE THIS CRATE'S READY TO ROLL?

JUST AS SOON AS DUAL AND NAMTAC CAN UN-JAM THESE GUNS THEY SABOTAGED, BUCK!

YEAH -- BUT IT'S SLOW WORK, ROGERS -- MAY TAKE ANOTHER HOUR!

OKAY, DUAL -- BUT I WARN YOU -- NO STALLING! REMEMBER -- WHEN I START TRADING FIREWORKS WITH YOUR PAL POUNCE, YOU TWO BIRDS WILL BE WITH ME --- SO THE BETTER THOSE GUNS WORK, THE LONGER YOU'LL KEEP BREATHING!

THE GUNS ARE DELAYING THINGS, DOC! WHAT'S POUNCE'S POSITION NOW?

LAT. 61-Z - LON. 94-X ... THIRD LEVEL! HE'S COMING LIKE A GREASED METEOR, BUCK! ONLY TWENTY MINUTES AWAY!

WHAT?? WE CAN'T BE READY THAT SOON! WE'LL HAVE TO HIDE THIS SHIP -- ANYTHING TO STALL FOR TIME!

TOO LATE EVEN FOR THAT, BUCK! WAIT! WHAT'S UP? POUNCE IS TURNING BACK! BUT --- WHY?

AND - OUT IN SPACE -

WELL, WELL ... EARTH TRANSPORTS ... LOADED WITH MEN AND SUPPLIES --- AND BOUND FOR THE MOON! WHAT A COINCIDENCE!

A SIMPLE BLUFF WILL VERIFY MY SUSPICIONS!

ATTENTION, TRANSPORTS! I'VE COME TO ESCORT YOU TO HUER'S URANIUM FIELDS! HE AND ROGERS ARE EXPECTING YOU!

TRANSPORT TO ESCORT CRAFT --- THERE'S SOME MISTAKE --- MY SHIPS CARRY 4,000 EARTH COLONISTS -- MEN, WOMEN AND CHILDREN -- TO PLANET VENUS -- MUCH OBLIGED FOR YOUR TROUBLE ---

WELL WORTH IT, COMMANDER ... IF YOU'LL ALLOW ME TO -- ER - PHOTOGRAPH YOUR SHIPS! NICE ACTION SHOT, EH? READY, NOW --- HOLD THAT POSE -- HAHAHAHA

HEH! GOOD HEAVENS ... WHAT WAS THAT VIBRATION? NEARLY DEAFENED ME! STRANGE, BUCK ... BUT FOR A MOMENT THE MAGNO-RADAR SHOWED TWO ADDITIONAL SHIPS ... BIG ONES ... BUT NOW THERE'S JUST THE ONE WE DETECTED BEFORE ... AND COMING TOWARD US AGAIN ... FASTER THAN EVER!!

TO BE CONT'D

DICK CALKINS & RICK YAGER

BATTLE ON THE MOON

1. HA! IT WON'T BE LONG NOW, ROGERS! WHEREVER YOU ARE, YOU'D BETTER SPEND THE FINAL MINUTES IN PRAYER ···· FOR I, COMMODORE POUNCE, HAVE COME TO ENGAGE YOU IN COMBAT ··· YOUR *LAST* COMBAT!

2. HMM ··· MOON AZIMUTH TO ZENITH ··· MINUS 30 x 40 DEGREES ··· WEST HEMISPHERE ··· LAT. 64 ··· LON. 30 ·····AH! I SEE IT NOW ··· A SHIP ··· *ROGERS' SHIP!!*

3. WHAT'S THE LATEST DOPE ON POUNCE, DOC? IS HE GETTING CLOSE?

CLOSE? GREAT HEAVENS, BUCK ··· HE'S ONLY FIVE MINUTES AWAY ·· AND COMING LIKE A GREASED COMET!

HOLY SMOKES, BUCK ··· YOU HAVEN'T A CHANCE! THE GUNS AREN'T READY YET!

4. OH, YES THEY ARE! DUAL AN' NAMTAC FINALLY GOT THEM SHOOTIN'-IRONS UN-JAMMED! YER ALL SET, BUCK!

SWELL, BARNEY! QUICK, NOW - LOCK THOSE TWO JOKERS IN THE NOSE COCK-PIT SO THEY'LL GET A RING-SIDE VIEW OF THE FIGHT THEY PROMOTED --

5. ··THEN·· EVERYBODY OFF THE SHIP! AND I'D BETTER SAY SO-LONG, JUST IN CASE --!

HEH ·· WELL ·· HERE'S HAPPY LANDINGS, BUCK! COME, MISS FORTUNE!

'BYE, BUCK!

6. WAL ··· ALL SET, BUCK! SO LONG! OH YEAH! ONE MORE THING ··· HERE'S THAT MYSTERIOUS "SECRET WEAPON" I BEEN SAVIN' FER THIS MOMENT ·····IT'S JEST AN' OL' D'PARTED PAL ··· WHO'S GOIN' ALONG T'HELP YUH WIN!

7. ··AHEM·· WAL GUESS I'LL BE GOIN'!

Too mi frend mister Buck Rogers·· His greatest fren in the hole world·· from admiral Cornplaster

8. THEN·· SUDDENLY –

9. ATTENTION, BELOW ····· I AM COMMODORE POUNCE ··· OF MARS!! I'VE COME TO CHALLENGE BUCK ROGERS TO COMBAT ···· IF HE IS NOT TOO COWARDLY TO MEET ME!!

10. AND NOW, ROGERS, IF YOU'RE PREPARED TO DIE, I'LL SIGNAL THE START OF BATTLE WITH A BOMB CONTAINING A CAPTIVE EARTH-PILOT ······A FITTING TOKEN OF MY CONTEMPT FOR *ALL* EARTHMEN! READ-D-D-Y ·······

COPYRIGHT 1947
JOHN F. DILLE
CO.

11. THERE! BOMBS AWAY, EH? HA HA HA HA HA ····· NOW, BUCK ROGERS, YOU DOOMED CUR ··· AT THE INSTANT OF EXPLOSION, I SHALL ATTACK YOU ··· READY OR NOT! I ASK NO QUARTER ··· AND I SHALL GIVE NONE!

12. POUNCE RECEIVES NO ANSWER ··· FOR BUCK IS NOT IN A "TALKING MOOD"! BUT THE FIRE SMOULDERING IN BUCK'S EYES BURNS AS BRIGHTLY AS THE FLAME FROM THE ROARING ROCKETS WHICH SEND HIM BLAZING INTO THE SKY TO ACCEPT POUNCE'S INSULTING CHALLENGE! *THE FIGHT IS ON!!*

TO BE
CONTINUED

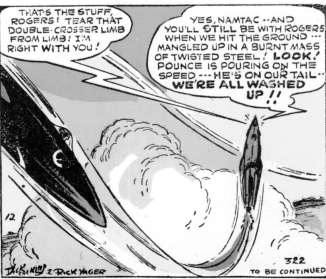

BATTLE ON THE MOON

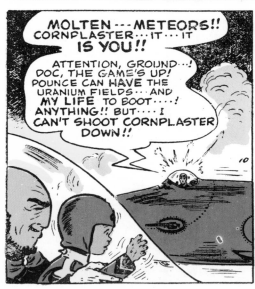

BUCK ROGERS IN THE 25th CENTURY

BATTLE ON THE MOON

MISTAKENLY THINKING VICTORY OVER BUCK ROGERS WAS CERTAIN, COMMODORE POUNCE RADIOED HIS H.Q. ON PLANET MARS TO SEND A POWERFUL TASK FORCE TO TAKE OVER EARTH'S VAST URANIUM DEPOSITS ON THE MOON. HERE COME THE MARTIANS——

BUT-- ON THE MOON-- THE TIDE OF BATTLE HAS TURNED—

POUNCE'S LATEST TRICK FIZZLED OUT LIKE ALL TH' OTHERS, DOC! BUCK'S GOT TH' LITTLE WEASEL ON TH' DEFENSIVE AG'IN!

YES--- LOOK! BUCK'S CLOSING IN FOR THE KILL! THIS IS THE PAY-OFF!

OKAY, POUNCE---- NOW THAT YOUR BAG OF DIRTY TRICKS IS EMPTY, LET'S SEE HOW YOU CAN TAKE IT WHEN THINGS ARE ON THE LEVEL!

IF YOU HAVE WORDS TO WASTE, ROGERS, YOU BETTER RADIO A LAST FAREWELL TO YOUR PALS ON THE MOON! YOU'RE A DEAD DUCK!

AND THERE'S THE BEGINNING OF THE END, ROGERS! A NICE LEFT-WING DRAG TO PULL YOU OFF CENTER!

WHILE I'M CRYING MY EYES OUT, POUNCE, NOTICE WHAT'S HAPPENED TO YOUR TAIL-FEATHERS!

ARRRGHH! THAT X!!★★~== #LUCKY PARLOR-HERO! HE'S SMASHED MY ROCKET-ASSEMBLAGE! BUT--LOOK!--ROGERS IS RIGHT IN POSITION FOR MY CORKSCREW-REVERSE ATTACK! READ-O-DY--...... NOW!

DOCTOR HUER! OH·H·· POOR BUCK! HE'S BEEN HIT-- KILLED! HE'S PLUNGING DOWN---OUT OF CONTROL!

HEH! STEADY, MISS FORTUNE! DON'T GIVE UP YET! BUCK NEVER DOES!

DOC, ISN'T BUCK PULLIN' HIS OLD "CRIPPLED-HAWK" TRICK-- HE IS! SURE HE IS!

SATAN'S BEARD! ROGERS !/-- YOU'RE NOT HUMAN! YOU'RE DEAD AND YOU DON'T KNOW IT!

IT MUST BE TRUE, IF YOU SAY SO, PEANUT! AH! I SEE YOU'RE OUT FOR A BREATH OF FRESH AIR, TOO!

CHATTER ON, STUPID-- WHILE YOU'RE STILL ABLE-- BECAUSE YOU'LL BE SILENT FOR A LONG TIME, WHEN YOUR SHATTERED CARCASS DECORATES ONE OF THOSE CRATER SLOPES.

WHAT A TOUCHING DESCRIPTION OF MY SAD ENDING! YOU SHOULD WRITE BOOKS, POUNCE!

HEY! TELL YOUR SHIP IT ISN'T POLITE TO YAWN IN PUBLIC!

X!★★@~~!XX# !!... THAT DID IT! THIS JUNK HEAP WON'T FLY MUCH LONGER! ROGERS HAS FINISHED ME!--

---- NO! WAIT! I FORGOT Z-2!! YES-S-S-S-S Z-2!! "HAH! SO, I'M STILL VERY MUCH IN THE FIGHT! YES--- INDEED!

HMM-- IF ONLY I CAN GET ROGERS TO LAY-OFF FOR A MINUTE ---I'LL HAVE HIM!--

AHEM:... ATTENTION, ROGERS! I CALL ON YOU, AS A SPORTSMAN, TO CEASE FIRING--- AND CONSIDER THE PROPOSITION, I THE LOSER, WISH TO MAKE!

OKAY, POUNCE, BECAUSE YOU'RE LICKED AND YOU KNOW IT-- I'LL HOLD FIRE--- AND IF YOUR REQUEST IS FOR MERCY-- WELL,-- START TALKING!

THANKS--

...SUCKER!! HA HA HA HA HA HA

H'RAY!! BUCK'S DONE IT, DOC! HE'S GOT POUNCE LICKED TO A STAND-STILL! TH' FIGHT'S OVER!!

HEH! IT DOES LOOK THAT WAY, BARNEY---

---HEH! POUNCE'S SHIP IS A SHATTERED HULK----AND THEY'VE STOPPED FIRING, BARNEY. BUT POUNCE IS AS UNPREDICTABLE AS A WOUNDED LEOPARD! I'LL HOLD MY CHEERS TILL I'M CERTAIN!

POUNCE, I GUESS YOU REALIZE THE GAME'S UP! I'LL COMPLY WITH YOUR REQUEST, AND HOLD FIRE--- TILL I HEAR WHAT YOU WANT TO SAY! OKAY--- START TALKING!

SUCKER! NOW YOU'LL LEARN ABOUT MY "LITTLE JUNIOR" Z-2!! HAHAHAHA...

--AHEM!! THANKS, ROGERS! YES, I ADMIT DEFEAT---THE FIRST OF MY CAREER! I SALUTE YOU, THE VICTOR, ROGERS!

SO FAR, THIS SOUNDS LIKE THE OLD STALL! COME TO THE POINT, POUNCE!

ALL RIGHT, ROGERS! AS YOU CAN SEE, IT'D BE SUICIDE TO TRY LANDING MY SHIP IN ITS BATTERED CONDITION! I REQUEST A FREE LANDING--ON A FLYING BELT---WITHOUT BEING SHOT AT BY YOUR PALS ON THE GROUND!

REQUEST GRANTED, POUNCE! GET GOING!

OKAY, ROGERS! BUT I HAVE NO FLYING BELT UP HERE! I'LL HAVE TO GO BELOW! KEEP FAR BEHIND ME, ROGERS, FOR--- ER---SAFETY'S SAKE----WHEN I BAIL OUT!

I'LL GIVE YOU THREE MINUTES, AND PLENTY OF ROOM, POUNCE!

AH! Z-2! MY "LITTLE JUNIOR" OCTO-JET! NOW--- THE LAUNCHING CONTROLS! I'LL SET THEM FOR 30 SECONDS!

MOST DEADLY CRAFT FOR HER SIZE, EVER BUILT! BLINDING SPEED---AND THE FIRE-POWER OF A HEAVY CRUISER!!

HMM--LISTEN TO THOSE ROCKETS HUM --26--27--28--29 ---REA-D-DY

MEANWHILE-BLAZING ACROSS SPACE IN ANSWER TO POUNCE'S CALL FOR AID, A POWERFUL MARTIAN TASK FORCE ROARS EVER NEARER TO THE MOON—

THIS IS THE GREATEST VICTORY OF COMMODORE POUNCE'S LONG CAREER! SINGLE-HANDED, THE MASTER HAS DEFEATED BUCK ROGERS AND HIS MEN, AND CLAIMED THE MOON'S URANIUM FIELDS FOR MARS!

COPYRIGHT 1947 JOHN F. DILLE CO.

BUT-AT THIS SAME MOMENT- IN EARTH'S MILITARY INTELLIGENCE H.Q.-- WASHINGTON, D.C.---

URGENT MESSAGE, SIR! OUTER-SPACE SCOUT SHIP 87 REPORTS 25 MARTIAN BATTLE CRUISERS---HEADED FOR THE MOON! ISN'T THAT WHERE HUER AND ROGERS ARE, SIR?

YES--! SOMEHOW THE URANIUM SECRET HAS LEAKED OUT--

--- SO WE'RE MOVING IN!

ATTENTION, COMMANDER--GOLDEN-EAGLE FIGHTER SQUADRON 13-- PREPARE TO TAKE OFF AT ONCE! OBJECTIVE--- MOON!!

DICK CALKINS   RICK YAGER

TO BE CONTINUED

BATTLE ON THE MOON

ON THE MOON, BUCK ROGERS AND COMMODORE POUNCE, THE MARTIAN, ARE STILL LOCKED IN DEADLY ROCKET-COMBAT···· A FIGHT IN WHICH ONLY BUCK'S MARVELOUS FLYING SKILL HAS SAVED HIM FROM POUNCE'S MURDEROUS, TREACHERY····

BUT— UNKNOWN TO EITHER COMBATANT, TWO POWERFUL TASK FORCES CONVERGE TOWARD THE MOON FROM THEIR RESPECTIVE PLANETS! ONE FORCE, FROM MARS, IS MOVING IN TO POUNCE'S AID····· THE OTHER FLEET, FROM EARTH, IS SPEEDING TO INTERCEPT THEM!

BUCK ROGERS AND COMMODORE POUNCE.

EARTH

EARTH'S CRACK "GOLDEN-EAGLE" FIGHTER SQUADRON NO. 13

MARS

MARTIAN FLEET ——— 25 BATTLE CRUISERS! A LONG HEAD-START PUTS THEM AS CLOSE TO THE MOON AS THE EARTH SQUADRON 15.

DISTANCE TO EARTH - 238,857 MILES

MOON

DISTANCE TO MARS - 47,761,143 MILES

DOC! DIDN'T I **TELL** YUH? IT'S ALL OVER! POUNCE IS LICKED! BUCK WINS!

HEH! YES, BARNEY, POUNCE'S SHIP IS SMASHED BEYOND USE! IT LOOKS AS THOUGH BUCK'S WAITING FOR HIM TO ABANDON SHIP····· AND SURRENDER!

BUT— AS BUCK WAITS FOR POUNCE TO BAIL OUT OF HIS BATTERED SHIP ON A **FLYING BELT**···

HUH!?? AM I··· SEEING THINGS??

HA HA HA HA HA HA NO, ROGERS····YOU **AREN'T!** THANKS FOR LETTING ME GO BELOW FOR A····· "FLYING BELT"! MIGHTY THOUGHTFUL OF YOU, GALAHAD! AND MIGHTY STUPID! IT'LL COST YOU YOUR LIFE, ROGERS!

POUNCE, YOU YELLOW DOUBLE-DEALER! SO THIS IS HOW YOU FOLLOW THE INTERPLANETARY ARTICLES OF WAR AND SURRENDER! BEG FOR MERCY LIKE A SQUEALING RAT····JUST TO GAIN AN ADVANTAGE!

THIS IS A FIGHT, YOU SIMPLE-MINDED PUNK···· NOT A TEA PARTY!

YES···NO USE KIDDING MYSELF··THAT IRON-PEANUT POUNCE IS FLYING, IS GREASED LIGHTNING WITH A DEADLY WALLOP! BUT POUNCE WON'T PICK ME OFF JUST YET! OH, NO! HE'LL SHOW OFF HIS NEW TOY FIRST···AND **I KNOW HOW!**

ATTENTION, PROFESSOR HUER!! DOC····CAN'T BEAT POUNCE··· END IS COMING UNLESS I GET HELP! CAN'T OUT-MANEUVER HIS FAST SHIP! GOODBYE!

HA! I HEARD YOU, ROGERS! SO YOU **KNOW** YOU HAVEN'T LONG TO LIVE, EH? BUT CHEER UP! YOUR PALS HAVE EVEN **LESS** TIME! **ONLY** AS MUCH AS IT TAKES ME TO LOCATE THEIR HIDE-OUT ROCK!

POUNCE'S H.Q-LOO

HEH! GET **THAT**, BARNEY? WHEN BUCK SAYS "PROFESSOR" HUER·····IT'S **CODE!** EVERY THIRD WORD AFTER "DOC"!

DOC····CAN'T BEAT **POUNCE**···END IS COMING UNLESS I **GET**···HELP! CAN'T **OUT**·MANEUVER HIS **FAST**·SHIP! GOODBYE!

QUICK! FLYIN'-BELTS! ON TH' DOUBLE!

AH! YOUR FRIENDS HIDE **WELL**, ROGERS····· BUT THEY DON'T FOOL **POUNCE!** HAHAHAHAHAHA **ROAST!** ROAST, YOU COWARDLY RABBITS! HA! **THAT** DOES IT!

COPYRIGHT 1947 JOHN F. DILLE CO.

WELL····**NOW**, GLAMOUR BOY, I CAN CONCENTRATE ENTIRELY ON····· **YOU**···EH?

?HUH?? WHERE···· **WHERE IS HE?**

POUNCE'S H.Q-LOO

331 TO BE CONTINUED

CAREFUL, POUNCE····IT'S USUALLY AT THIS STAGE OF A BATTLE THAT BUCK HATCHES A "ROGERS SPECIAL"·····ONE OF THOSE SUDDEN, LIGHTNING STROKES THAT ENEMIES LIKE **YOU** SELDOM LIVE TO TELL ABOUT!

RICK YAGER

BATTLE ON THE MOON

ABOARD THE FLAGSHIP OF EARTH'S "GOLDEN-EAGLE" FIGHTER SQUADRON 13 ···BOUND FOR THE MOON—

ATTENTION! COMMANDER FLINT TO ALL SHIPS ······ GUN CREWS REPORT TO READY ROOMS FOR BRIEFING ··· REMAIN AT ALERT, TO MAN BATTLE STATIONS ···· AT '0600 FALL INTO ATTACK-FORMATION 654-H···· THAT IS ALL····

AND ···FLASHING AT TOP SPEED TOWARD THE MOON FROM THE OPPOSITE DIRECTION···MARS···

TASK FORCE M-E-ZERO-W···· ATTENTION ···· STRONG EARTH UNIT REPORTED RACING TOWARD POUNCE'S POSITION ON MOON TO INTERCEPT US··· STAND-BY FOR BATTLE PLAN····

MEANWHILE, ON THE MOON, BUCK'S FIGHT WITH POUNCE IS TAKING AN ODD TURN - - →

DOC!! WHAT IN BLAZES IS BUCK TRYIN' TO DO ···COMMIT SUICIDE? BAILIN' OUT IN A BLASTED BOX ··· NO PERFECTION ··· NO SPEED ··· NO NOTHIN'··· 'CEPT CERTAIN DEATH!

BARNEY, I'M NOT SURE ···BUT I THINK BUCK HAS PULLED A FATAL BONER! WHATEVER BUCK'S STRATEGY WAS ··· IT'S BACKFIRED! POUNCE HAS HIM ··· IT'S ONLY A MATTER OF SECONDS!

NO! LOOK, DOC!

HEH?

WELL, MR. BUCK ROGERS ···MR. PARLOR HERO··· THIS ENDS A LONG, BRILLIANT CAREER OF NEWSPAPER CLIPPINGS ··· SHOWING YOU LOOKING BRAVE AND ROMANTIC, EH? BUT IT'S ALL OVER NOW! AND HERE'S YOUR TICKET TO ETERNITY!

"NEWS REPORT"···"GLAMOUR BOY MEETS DEATH"··· BUCK ROGERS, PAMPERED HERO TO ARM-CHAIR ADVENTURERS AND SOCIETY MATRONS, MET COMMODORE POUNCE OF MARS! PLEASE OMIT FLOWERS"··· HA HA HA HA HA HA

FRY! COOK! BROIL AND ROAST ··· YOU WHITE-LIVERED HOT-HOUSE FLOWER!

NOW··· UP AND AROUND! I'LL SIZZLE YOU ONCE MORE FOR GOOD MEASURE ··· THEN——

HUH?? WHAT AILS THIS STUPID SHIP? IT WON'T RESPOND! IT DOESN'T PULL UP! FEELS LIKE I'M BEING PUSHED DOWNWARD! I'M ··· I'M GOING TO CR····

WHAT?? HOW DID ROGERS' SHIP GET BEHIND ME? AND THAT FORCE-RAY···COMING FROM ROGERS' SHIP! HOW?? NOONE'S ABOARD THAT SHIP NOW! ROGERS WAS IN THE BOX! HE'S DEAD!

···N-NOW ROGERS' SHIP IS···· IS LANDING!! A ···P-PERFECT LANDING··· ALL BY ITSELF! IMPOSSIBLE····· ····WITHOUT A ·PILOT!

COPYRIGHT 1948 JOHN F. DILLE CO.

WAIT!! THAT HATCH DOOR! IS····IS IT SLOWLY··· OPENING?·· OR·· OR DO I JUST IMAGINE·· HUH···

RICK YAGER

TO BE CONTINUED

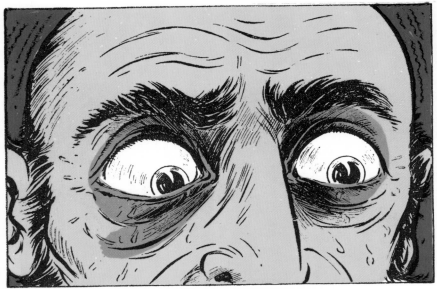

NO! NO! IMPOSSIBLE! THAT **CAN'T** BE ROGERS! **ROGERS IS DEAD!** I KILLED HIM! BURNED HIM TO A CRISP! MY EYES DECEIVE ME···· THIS IS JUST AN AN ILLUSION! A TRICK OF THE NERVES··· AFTER THE GRUELLING STRAIN OF BATTLE!

IF YOU THINK I'M "JUST AN ILLUSION," POUNCE··· WAIT TILL I GET MY THUMBS ON YOUR ADAM'S-APPLE!

YOU THOUGHT I WAS IN THAT BOX YOU DESTROYED, POUNCE···· BUT HOW COULD I HAVE WRAPPED CHAINS AROUND THE **OUTSIDE** OF THE BOX, ONCE I WAS **INSIDE??** PUZZLING, ISN'T IT?

SO NOW OUR LITTLE GAME OF TAG REACHES A CLIMAX··· BUT I'VE ALREADY GUESSED THE OUTCOME!

THEN, BY THE BEARD OF THE VEILED WIZARD, YOU'D BETTER GUESS **AGAIN**, ROGERS! I'LL **GET YOU YET!**

I CAN'T GET THIS JUNK-HEAP INTO THE AIR···· BUT I **CAN** GAIN SOME DISTANCE··· AND TIME! TIME TO PREPARE! YES-S-S THAT'S ALL **I** WANT!

HA!! NOT MUCH FIGHT **LEFT** IN ROGERS··· OR HE'D HAVE RETURNED FIRE!

HMMM··· OR·· OR COULD THAT ONE-TRACK STUPID ACTUALLY BE HOPING TO GET HIS FILTHY FINGERS AROUND MY··· MY··· *GULP*·····

LUCK OF SATAN!! *!#~◦!

WELL··· AT LEAST I HAVE A HALF-MILE LEAD ON THAT SCOWLING FER-DE-LANCE! *BR-R-R* THOSE EYES! GRAY··· COLD··· LIKE DISCS OF FROZEN DEVIL-FIRE! ARRGH!

WHAT AM I SAYING?!!

ACTUALLY, THE COWARD'S DEATHLY AFRAID OF ME! BUT TERROR PLAYS STRANGE TRICKS ON COWARDS! SOME RUN··· WHILE OTHERS ADVANCE BLINDLY TOWARD THE POWER THEY KNOW WILL DESTROY THEM!

YES! THAT'S IT! IT'S **FEAR** THAT DRAWS ROGERS TO ME!

···AND YET··· THOSE EYES! INSTEAD OF BULGING WITH FEAR··· THEY SMOULDERED WITH··· WITH···

BOSH!! LET'S SEE NOW·· RADIO···· RATIONS···· WEAPONS!

NOW TO SET UP AN AMBUSH! A DEATH-TRAP! **HUH??** HOW DID ROGERS GET HERE SO FAST ??······· OH! A **FLYING BELT!!** CURSE HIM··· THAT GIVES ROGERS A DEADLY ADVANTAGE!···· AND HE **KNOWS** IT!!

BUT EVEN WITH THAT··· I DOUBT HE HAS THE COURAGE TO FOLLOW ME!

COPYRIGHT 1948 JOHN F. DILLE CO.

RICK YAGER

334 TO BE CONTINUED

4

PACT OF PERPETUAL PEACE

YOU GO AS ENVOYS TO THE FORBIDDEN CITY, IN MONGOLIA, WHERE THE "CELESTIAL MOGUL" REIGNS AS OVERLORD OF OUR PRISONER, THE EMPEROR, AND OF THE VICEROY WHO HAS SEIZED HIS POWER. YOU MUST GO AS CHILIANS, FOR HE HOLDS AMERICANS AS SLAVES OF HIS VASSAL, THE EMPEROR.

MORKE KA LONO WAS TO GO WITH ME AS ADVISOR. A REBEL, HIS INTERESTS WERE OURS

LIU, ALSO A MONGOL REBEL, WAS TO COME AS COMPANION OF WILMA

ENRIQUE, WHO HAD BEEN CAPTURED WITH MORKE, WAS TO COUNSEL US IN CHILIAN AFFAIRS

(COPYRIGHT JOHN DILLE CO.)

IF YOU WENT TO MONGOLIA AS AMERICANS, YOU WOULD BE KILLED

WE TAKE SOME KILLING, LIU

THE SENORITA IS — WHAT YOU SAY — A TOUGH EGG?

SO WE LEFT FOR CHILI, ON THE FIRST LEG OF OUR ADVENTURE

(TO BE CONTINUED)

WE ARRIVED AT THE CHILIAN CAPITAL WITHOUT INCIDENT. MACGREGOR HAD ARRANGED THINGS WITH THE CHILIAN GOVERNMENT —

WILL WE BE SEASICK CAPTAIN?

NOT AT ALL. WE'LL SELDOM COME TO THE SURFACE.

HELLO, SOL, OLD CHAP.

WE BOARDED A SUB TO CROSS UNDER THE PACIFIC TO MONGOLIA

(COPYRIGHT JOHN DILLE CO.)

DOWN THE SUBMARINE TUNNEL WE WENT, FROM CRATER LAKE, THROUGH THE WATER LOCK, AND OUT INTO THE OCEAN.

WHAT IS THAT?

WHERE?

(TO BE CONTINUED)

GREY AND GHOSTLY, THE SUBMARINE'S SEARCHLIGHT SHOWED THE WRECK OF A SHIP

I'VE NEVER SEEN THE LIKE

IT'S A 20TH CENTURY SURFACE SHIP — MAYBE A GERMAN RAIDER OF THE WORLD WAR

WE'LL EXPLORE THE WHOLE WRECK

THIS IS A LIQUID AIR BLAST, LIKE YOUR ROCKET TUBES, YOU CAN SWIM LIKE TINY SUBMARINES IN THESE FLEXIBLE, STEEL SUITS.

I FEEL MORE LIKE A FISH

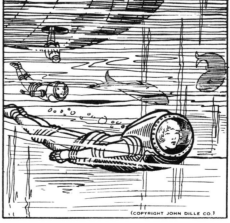

(COPYRIGHT JOHN DILLE CO.)

WILMA REACHED THE WRECK FIRST. WE HEARD HER RADIOED SCREAM AS SLIMY TENACLES REACHED OUT AND WRAPPED AROUND HER

(TO BE CONTINUED)

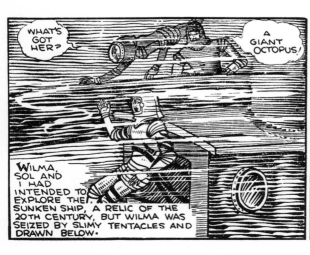

WHAT'S GOT HER?

A GIANT OCTOPUS!

WILMA, SOL AND I HAD INTENDED TO EXPLORE THE SUNKEN SHIP, A RELIC OF THE 20TH CENTURY, BUT WILMA WAS SEIZED BY SLIMY TENTACLES AND DRAWN BELOW.

FIGHT, WILMA! WE'RE COMING

CAN'T FIGHT IT'S TOO STRONG FOR ME!

BE CAREFUL!

FORTUNATELY THE MONSTER COULDN'T CRUSH WILMA'S SUIT.

(COPYRIGHT JOHN DILLE CO.)

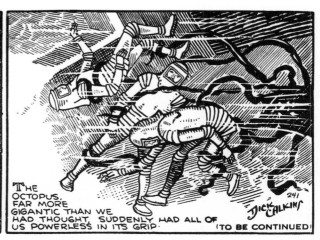

THE OCTOPUS, FAR MORE GIGANTIC THAN WE HAD THOUGHT, SUDDENLY HAD ALL OF US POWERLESS IN ITS GRIP.

(TO BE CONTINUED)

HOW THIS FISH CAN **HUG!** OH I'M FAINTING

OUR STEEL RIBS SEEMED READY TO SNAP

HOW CAN WE FIGHT THIS THING, SOL?

I'LL SHOW YOU IF I CAN GET AN ARM FREE

HA! I'LL UNWRAP MYSELF YET!

HOLD YOUR BREATHS! HERE GOES AN ATOMIC TORPEDO AT HIM!

OUR HELMET RADIOS WERE WORKING WELL.

THE EXPLOSION WAS TERRIFIC. WE LOST CONSCIOUSNESS

BLAM!

242 (TO BE CONTINUED)

WE HAD LOST CONSCIOUSNESS WHEN SOL'S ATOMIC TORPEDO EXPLODED, AND WERE BLOWN OUT THROUGH THE HATCH OF THE SUNKEN SHIP

WHEN I CAME TO I WAS ON THE OCEAN BED, NEAR THE WRECK, AND NOT A LEAK IN MY SUIT!

WOW! THAT ATOMIC TORPEDO SURE WAS JUST TOO BAD. WONDER WHERE THE OTHERS ARE

I ROUNDED THE BOW OF THE WRECK. SOL WAS HELPING WILMA TO HER FEET

BUT WE WERE "DEAF AND DUMB". THE CONCUSSION HAD DERANGED OUR DELICATE HELMET RADIOS. HOW COULD WE SIGNAL THE SUBMARINE HANGING SOMEWHERE IN THE OCEAN ABOVE US? HOW TO FIND IT??

243 (TO BE CONTINUED)

WITH OUR HELMET RADIOS OUT OF COMMISSION, WE COULD COMMUNICATE ONLY BY GESTURES.

MY PLAN MAY WORK

OH, I'M SO WEAK

POOR DARLING! SHE'S ABOUT ALL IN.

I SEE NO SENSE IN SOL'S ACTIONS BUT I'LL GIVE HIM A LIFT

WHAT IN THE WORLD ARE THEY DOING

I CAN'T IMAGINE HOW AN ANCHOR IS GOING TO HELP US REACH A SUBMARINE FLOATING SOMEWHERE IN THE OCEAN ABOVE US —

244 (TO BE CONTINUED)

FINALLY I GATHERED THAT SOL WANTED TO SWING THE ANCHOR AGAINST THE SIDE OF THE WRECK.

NOW I THINK I UNDERSTAND

THEN I REALIZED SOL'S PURPOSE. WE WERE MAKING A SIGNAL BELL OUT OF THE STEEL SIDES OF THE SHIP

BONG! BONG!

SOUND CARRIES FAR UNDER WATER

MUFFLED BUT VIBRANT, THE SOUND RANG OUT. WOULD A 25TH CENTURY SHIP HAVE A MERE SOUND SIGNAL RECEIVER? WOULD IT BE CLOSE ENOUGH TO "FEEL" THE VIBRATION THROUGH THE WATER?

BONG!

245 (TO BE CONTINUED)

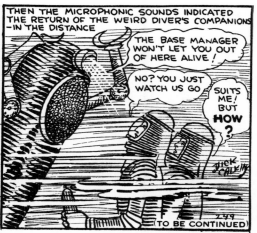

PACT OF PERPETUAL PEACE

TRAPPED INSIDE THE SUBMERGED WRECK, WE RISKED A CHANCE THAT AN ATOMIC TORPEDO MIGHT BREAK THE THIN STEEL HATCH

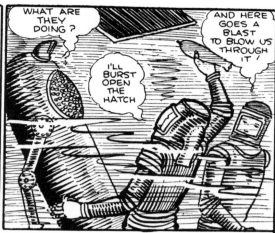

WHAT ARE THEY DOING?

I'LL BURST OPEN THE HATCH

AND HERE GOES A BLAST TO BLOW US THROUGH IT!

BLAM!

(COPYRIGHT JOHN DILLE CO.)

LOOK OUT ROGERS! HERE THEY COME!

OUR FRIEND IN THE STEAM BOILER HERE MUST BE UNCONSCIOUS

(TO BE CONTINUED)

WE HAD BEEN BLOWN THROUGH THE HATCH, ALMOST INTO THE ARMS OF THE RETURNING MONGOL DIVERS. WE DARED NOT SPEAK LEST THEY PICK UP OUR RADIO WAVES.

HERE WE ARE, MEN. THE OLD HULK'S LOOMING UP AHEAD.

C'MON, ROGERS—LET'S BLOW, TOOT SWEET!

YEAH—BUT HOW ABOUT THIS BOZO? WE CAN'T LEAVE HIM—HE'D SPILL TH' BEANS

YOU MEAN HE'D TELL THOSE JOKERS ABOUT US?

NOTHING DIFFERENT! AND THEY'D RADIO MONGOLIA THAT WE'D DISCOVERED THE SECRETS OF THE TREASURE HUNTERS

(COPYRIGHT JOHN DILLE CO.)

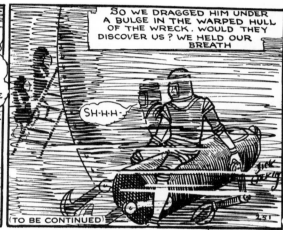

SO WE DRAGGED HIM UNDER A BULGE IN THE WARPED HULL OF THE WRECK. WOULD THEY DISCOVER US? WE HELD OUR BREATH

SH-H-H-

(TO BE CONTINUED)

NONE OF THE MONGOL DEEP-SEA TREASURE-HUNTERS SAW US AS THEY TROUPED INTO THEIR CAMOUFLAGED BASE IN THE ANCIENT WRECK

HEAVE HO!

SO SOL AND I, DRAGGING OUR UNCONSCIOUS PRISONER WITH US, "BLEW" FOR THE RENDEVOUS, SIGNALLING FAINTLY FOR OUR SUB

IT MUST BE JAMMED

WE'LL OPEN IT WITH THE DRILLS

WHAT IS THIS CRAZY CYLINDER WITH STEEL LEGS?

INSIDE THE SUB WE EXAMINED OUR PRIZE.

SAPRISTI! A GIRL!

SIZZLING ROCKETS!

IT'S LANLU!

(COPYRIGHT JOHN DILLE CO.)

252

(TO BE CONTINUED)

SOL AND I, EXPLORING A SUBMERGED WRECK, HAD CAPTURED A MONGOL DEEP-SEA DIVING MACHINE, AND BROUGHT IT BACK TO THE SUB WITH US. TO OUR SURPRISE, ITS OCCUPANT WAS LANLU, FORMER FAVORITE OF THE MONGOL EMPEROR. SHE WAS BADLY SHAKEN UP AND WILMA PUT HER TO BED IN A STATEROOM

BUT LANLU, WHAT WERE YOU DOING AT THE BOTTOM OF THE PACIFIC?

I WAS HIDING. WHEN BUCK CAPTURED KILLER KANE I WAS SUSPECTED OF AIDING HIM——

(COPYRIGHT JOHN DILLE CO.)

—SO I FLED FROM AMERICA TO MONGOLIA, WHERE I GOT A JOB WITH THE CELESTIAL MOGUL'S TREASURE HUNTING COMPANY WHICH GAVE ME A SUBMARINE HIDING PLACE

WE'RE GOING TO MONGOLIA, BUT YOU'LL BE SAFE ON OUR SUB

WHAT COURSE ARE YOU STEERING? I MUST SEE YOUR CAPTAIN AT ONCE!

WE'RE LAYING OUR COURSE NOR'WEST BY NORTH. WHAT OF IT

BUT THAT WILL TAKE YOU OVER FLEMING DEEP! OH, YOU MUSN'T! ALL OF US WILL BE LOST!

253

(TO BE CONTINUED)

PACT OF PERPETUAL PEACE

258

259 (TO BE CONTINUED)

260

261 (TO BE CONTINUED)

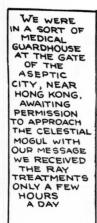

PACT OF PERPETUAL PEACE

THE WOMAN PHYSICIAN WHO HAD CHARGE OF US LOOKED ABOUT TWENTY FIVE YEARS OLD, BUT SHE TOLD US SHE WAS ONE HUNDRED TWENTY ONE. SHE HAD FINISHED HER MEDICAL COURSE AT FOURTEEN, AND HAD BEEN PRACTICING ONE HUNDRED AND SEVEN YEARS

DO YOU MEAN THAT BY KEEPING GERM-FREE YOU NEVER GROW OLD?

PRACTICALLY THAT. ALL INHABITANTS OF THE ASEPTIC CITY BELONG TO THE MEDICAL NOBILITY. WE CAN LIVE ALMOST FOREVER

(COPYRIGHT JOHN DILLE CO.)

WHY DON'T YOU GIVE YOUR COUNTRYMEN—AND **ALL MANKIND** THE BENEFIT OF YOUR KNOWLEDGE AND SCIENCE

WH-WHY, YOU TALK LIKE A SOCIALIST! OR—A **NORTH AMERICAN**

WELL WE **ARE** AMERICANS—BUCK ROGERS AND I!

AND PROUD OF IT!

SUFFERING DRAGONS! THEY HAVE SPILLED THE BEANS

HELP! GUARDS! GRAB THEM!

JICK CALKIN

(TO BE CONTINUED) 266

WE HAD NO WEAPONS, OF COURSE, AND QUICKLY WERE OVERPOWERED BY THE GUARD, WHO WERE THEMSELVES MYSTIFIED BY THE PANIC OF THE PHYSICIAN

OH, TO THINK THAT YOU—**YOU**—ARE THE **NOTORIOUS**, VIOLENT, **SAVAGE**, BUCK ROGERS! AND—AND **I LOVED YOU** I HAD DECIDED TO **MARRY** YOU!

GOSH! WHAT AN ESCAPE

WELL, I GUESS **I'D** HAVE SOMETHING TO SAY ABOUT **THAT**

SHE THEN BITTERLY ASSAILED **ME!**

(COPYRIGHT JOHN DILLE CO.)

WE HAVE BEEN DECEIVED! WE THOUGHT THEY WERE ALL CHILIANS! BUT THESE TWO ARE **AMERICANS!** SUMMON DUKE KALANG AT ONCE

IT SHALL BE DONE, CELESTIAL DOCTOR

WHAT'S THIS? THEY THINK TO FACE HIS ASEPTIC MAJESTY, THE CELESTIAL MOGUL HIMSELF? THESE LOW, SAVAGE, **FIGHTING AMERICANS?**

YES! WE FOUGHT FOR **HUMAN RIGHTS** IN 1776! AND IN 1917. **AND BY THE EAGLE OF FREEDOM WE** CAN DO IT ONCE **MORE IN 2530,** IF YOU CAN'T LISTEN TO REASON!

JICK CALKIN

(TO BE CONTINUED) 267

NOW TELL YOUR RULER WE **MUST** SEE AT ONCE

WELL THE RAY TREATMENTS WERE SUCCESSFUL THEY **ARE** ASEPTIC **NOW**

I'LL JUST PUT IT UP TO HIS MAJESTY HIMSELF

WILMA AND I WERE ALONE AT LAST FOR THE FIRST TIME IN MANY DAYS. BUT IN A LITTLE WHILE KALANG CAME BACK

OH BUCK, I'M SO NERVOUS THE FATE OF ALL MANKIND REALLY DEPENDS ON OUR SUCCESS

WELL, WHAT'S THE VERDICT?

STRANGELY ENOUGH, IT PLEASES HIS MAJESTY'S FANCY TO LOOK OVER SOME OF THESE WILD AMERICAN REBELS FROM HIS VASSAL EMPEROR'S DOMAIN HE WILL SEE YOU,

SO **THIS** IS THE PALACE FROM WHICH THE WORLD IS SUPPOSED TO BE RULED

IT'S GOOD LOOKING, ANYWAY.

HIS MAJESTY HAS LIVED HERE FOR 150 YEARS.

JICK CALKIN

268

WHAT FATE AWAITED US AND OUR MISSION WITHIN THESE WALLS?

THIS IS THE THRONE ROOM. WHEN HIS MAJESTY ENTERS YOU MUST PROSTRATE YOURSELVES AND STRIKE YOUR HEADS ON THE FLOOR THRICE

DAILY DOZEN STUFF, HUH?

BUCK, DON'T BE FLIPPANT

DOWN! DOWN! HE COMES

WHAT'S THE HURRY?

OH BUCK, BE CAREFUL!

BOW! BOW TO HIS ASEPTIC MAJESTY-CELESTIAL MOGUL OF MONGOLIA-POTENTIATE OF ASIA—DEAN OF THE EVER-LIVING NOBILITY—OVERLORD OF THE MONGOLIAN EMPERORS OF AMERICA AND EUROPE-WORLD RULER!!!

(COPYRIGHT JOHN DILLE CO.)

OH MOURNFUL DRAGONS! HEADS WILL FALL FOR THIS!

WE SALUTE YOU, SIR, IN THE NAME OF FREE AMERICA!

WHAT'S **THIS?!!!!** YOU DARE **STAND** IN OUR PRESENCE AND SPEAK OF "FREE AMERICA"?!!

JICK CALKIN

269

(TO BE CONTINUED)

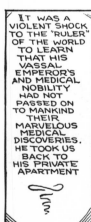

PACT OF PERPETUAL PEACE

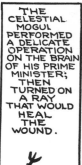

5
TIGER MEN OF MARS

BUCK ROGERS IN THE 25th CENTURY

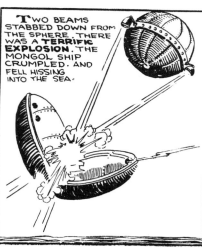

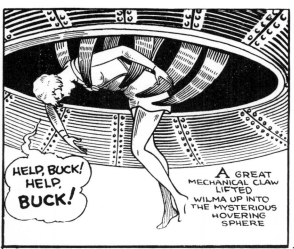

WILMA HAD BEEN CAPTURED BY MEN OF A STRANGE RACE, WHO HAD COME DOWN OUT OF THE SKY IN A MYSTERIOUS SPHERE OF METAL

THE MARTIANS HAD WITHDRAWN THEIR INTERPLANETARY SHIP SEVERAL THOUSAND MILES FROM EARTH WHILE THEY QUESTIONED WILMA.

WILMA WAS A PRISONER ABOARD THE SPACE SHIP OF THE TIGER MEN OF MARS, WHICH NOW HOVERED FAR ABOVE THE EARTH. WILMA FACED THE COMMANDER

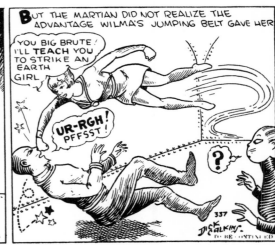

ANGERED BY THE TIGER MAN'S BLOW WILMA HAD KNOCKED HIM UNCONSCIOUS. SHE LEAPED THROUGH A DOOR INTO THE CONTROL ROOM OF THE MARTIAN SPACE SHIP. NOORY PURSUED HER.

WE HAD CRIPPLED THE TERRIBLE WEAPON OF THE UNEARTHLY SPHERE, AND WERE BEARING DOWN ON IT RAPIDLY, LITTLE DREAMING WILMA COULD BE ABOARD IT.

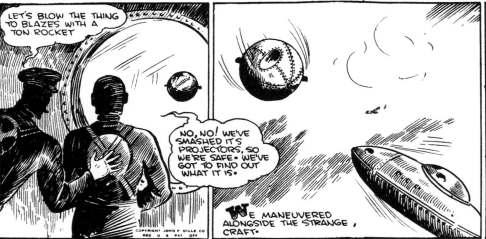

LET'S BLOW THE THING TO BLAZES WITH A TON ROCKET

NO, NO! WE'VE SMASHED ITS PROJECTORS, SO WE'RE SAFE. WE'VE GOT TO FIND OUT WHAT IT IS.

WE MANEUVERED ALONGSIDE THE STRANGE CRAFT.

AS WE NOSED UP TO THE OBSERVATION WINDOW OF THE MYSTERIOUS SHIP—

WILMA!

THE METAL HULL OF THAT SHIP CUTS OFF THE RADIO. I CAN'T TUNE HER IN, SIR.

343

TO BE CONTINUED

WILMA WAS UNABLE TO COMMUNICATE WITH US EXCEPT BY SIGNS, FOR THE METAL HULL OF THE SPHERE SHIP CUT OFF THE RADIO WAVES

WHAT DOES SHE MEAN? LOOKS LIKE SHE'S TRYING TO TELL US SOMETHING—

I THINK I UNDERSTAND HER, SIR

THE CAPTAIN INTERPRETED WILMA'S SIGNAL, SO WE SETTLED DOWN ON TOP OF THE UNEARTHLY CRAFT, AND GRAPPLED WITH A SUPER-ELECTRO MAGNET.

NOT A CHANCE, SIR, THIS HATCH JUST WON'T BE PRIED LOOSE

BUT I'VE GOT TO GET WILMA OUT OF THERE. WHAT'LL I DO?

THE DRILL DOESN'T MAKE A SCRATCH.

(TO BE CONTINUED) 344

WE HAD GRAPPLED WITH THE MYSTERIOUS SPHERE SHIP, BUT CROWBARS AND DRILLS HAD FAILED TO OPEN IT UP, SO———I DROPPED DOWN TO THE OBSERVATION WINDOW ON A ROPE.

OH BUCK, DEAREST.

WILMA, DARLING.

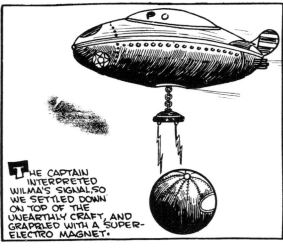

NEITHER SOUND NOR RADIO COULD PENETRATE THE SPHERICAL HULL, SO I WROTE MY MESSAGE FOR HER TO SEE

I'M GOING TO TAKE YOU TO NIAGARA

— SO WE ROCKETTED FULL BLAST FOR NIAGARA—

345

TO BE CONTINUED

AT LENGTH WE LANDED IN NIAGARA WITH OUR CAPTIVE SPHERE SHIP, IN WHICH WILMA WAS IMPRISONED AND WE ATTACKED IT WITH HIGH-POWER DRILLS, BUT ITS HARDNESS RESISTED ALL OUR EFFORTS

BLAZING ROCKETS! I'VE GOT TO GET WILMA OUT OF THAT UNEARTHLY THING SOMEHOW!

SHE'S MOTIONING US TO GET AWAY. I BET SHE HAS A PLAN.

ALL RIGHT! WE'LL BACK OFF AND SEE.

THIS FORCE-RAY OF THE MARTIANS OUGHT TO DO THE TRICK

CRASH!

346

TO BE CONTINUED

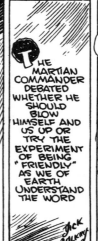

TIGER MEN OF MARS

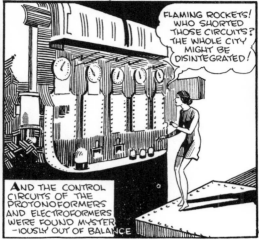

149

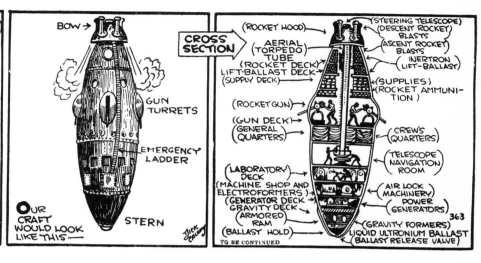

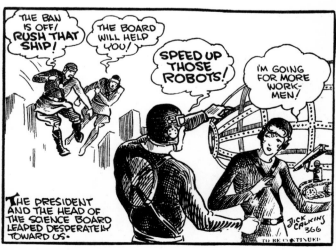

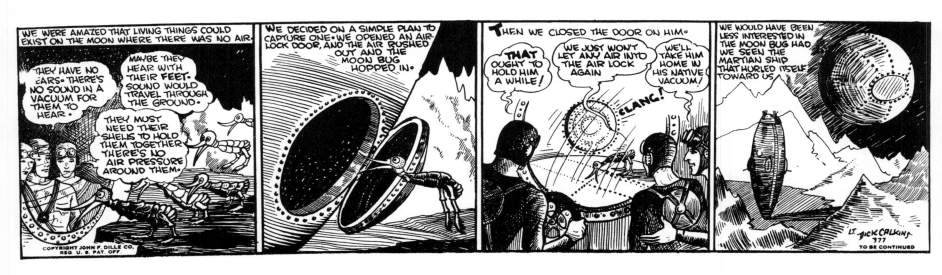

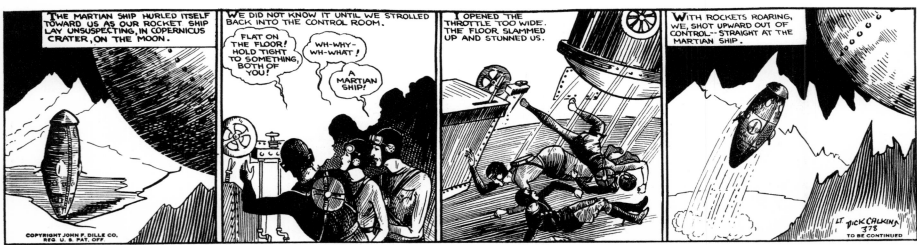

TIGER MEN OF MARS

IN THE TEST FLIGHT OF OUR INTERPLANETARY SHIP, WE HAD LANDED ON THE MOON. WHILE THERE A MARTIAN SHIP SUDDENLY LOOMED THREATENINGLY ABOVE US.

DAZED FROM THE JAR OF OUR TERRIFIC TAKE-OFF, WE ROCKETED FULL BLAST AT THE SPHERICAL CRAFT.

COPYRIGHT JOHN F. DILLE CO.

WHEN WE RECOVERED, I STAGGERED TO THE EMERGENCY CUT-OFF.

THERE! I'LL EASE OFF OUR SPEED A BIT.

WH-WHAT HAPPENED? DID WE HIT THE MARTIAN SHIP?

HAVE KNOCKED IT TO FLINDERS. WE MUST OUR NOSE PLATES ARE DENTED BUT SAFE

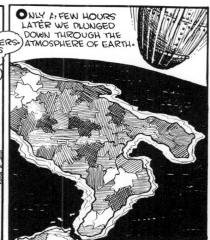

ONLY A FEW HOURS LATER WE PLUNGED DOWN THROUGH THE ATMOSPHERE OF EARTH.

WHY THAT LOOKS LIKE ITALY. WE'RE ON THE WRONG SIDE OF THE EARTH!

AND WE CAN'T SPEED HOME. AIR FRICTION WOULD BURN US UP. WHAT SHALL WE DO?

379
TO BE CONTINUED

WE HAD COME DOWN OVER ITALY. OUR PROBLEM WAS HOW TO GET BACK TO NIAGARA AT FULL SPEED WITHOUT SUFFERING FROM AIR FRICTION.

COPYRIGHT JOHN F. DILLE CO.
REG. U. S. PAT. OFF.

I ROCKETED UPWARD AND WESTWARD.

ABOVE THE STRATOSPHERE THERE WAS NO AIR. I COULD MAKE SPEED.

THEN I REVERSED THE SHIP AND DROPPED DOWN OVER NIAGARA.

ROARING CROWDS WELCOMED US.

QUICK, STODDARD! RUSH REPAIRS! LOAD SUPPLIES!

I'LL REPORT TO THE PRESIDENT RIGHT AWAY

DICK CALKINS
380
TO BE CONTINUED

WHILE SUPPLIES WERE RUSHED ABOARD—

COPYRIGHT JOHN F. DILLE CO.
REG. U. S. PAT. OFF.

WE MUSTERED OUR CREW FOR THE FIRST MARTIAN EXPEDITION EVER TO LEAVE EARTH—

I, MYSELF WAS CAPTAIN

I WAS FIRST MATE

I WAS SECOND MATE

I WAS CHIEF ENGINEER AND CHEMIST

I CAME ALONG AS ASTRONOMICAL NAVIGATOR AND GRAVITATIONIST

I WAS ELECTRONIST

I WAS CHIEF ROCKET GUNNER

BUCK ROGERS — WILMA DEERING — LIEUTENANT BURKE — PROFESSOR STODDARD — BOB BYRON — JOE MARTIN — JUD HANCOCK

WHAT'S THE DELAY?

THE PRESIDENT IS COMING! WE HAVE TO CHRISTEN THE SHIP PUBLICLY. WHAT SHALL WE CALL IT?

DICK CALKINS
381
TO BE CONTINUED

WE WERE ABOUT TO LAUNCH THE MOST DARING EXPEDITION EVER ATTEMPTED BY MAN — A TRIP TO MARS —TO RESCUE SALLY, WILMA'S LITTLE SISTER AND ILLANA THE GOLDEN PRINCESS, FROM THE HANDS OF THE SINISTER TIGER MEN WHO DOMINATED THAT PLANET.

COPYRIGHT JOHN F. DILLE CO.
REG. U. S. PAT. OFF.

FIRST, WILMA NAMED OUR ROCKET SHIP—

I CHRISTEN THEE SATELLITE!

WE RECEIVED A SPECIAL COMMISSION FROM THE PRESIDENT HIMSELF.

--AND WHATEVER BEFALLS, MAY YOU UNFALTERINGLY UPHOLD THE HONOR OF EARTH!

THEN WE SHOT SKYWARD, ON OUR FORTY SEVEN MILLION MILE JOURNEY THROUGH SPACE, TOWARD MARS— AND WE KNEW NOT WHAT!

382
LT. DICK CALKINS
TO BE CONTINUED

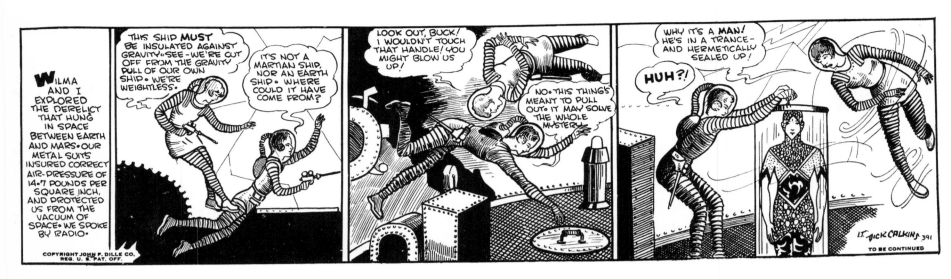

TIGER MEN OF MARS

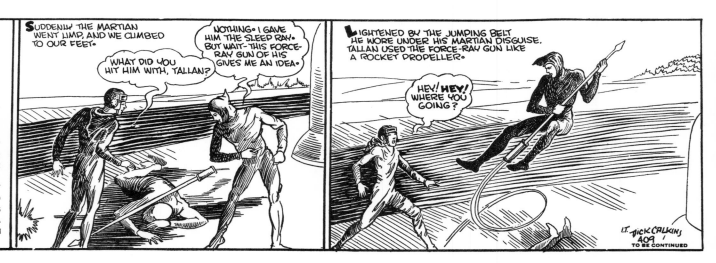

6
SUNKEN CITY OF ATLANTIS

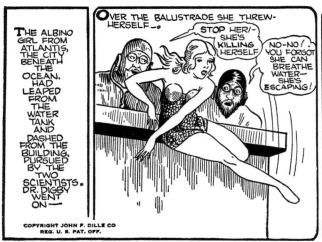

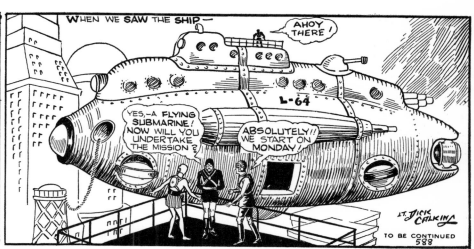

WILMA AND I HAD BEEN PUT IN COMMAND OF THE **FLYING SUB** OF THE DEPARTMENT OF SCIENCE, TO EXPLORE THE MYSTERIOUS CITY BENEATH THE OCEAN—ATLANTIS—BUT THE THIRD OFFICER, **ARDALA VALMAR**, HAD MADE OFF WITH THE SHIP WITHOUT EXPLANATION. WILMA AND I PURSUED—.

COPYRIGHT JOHN F. DILLE CO. REG. U.S. PAT. OFF.

THROUGH THE BLACK NIGHT WE **ZEEPED**—EASTWARD—.

I DON'T KNOW MUCH ABOUT HER, BUCK. SHE SEEMS LIKE A CLICKY KID — AND HER RECORD IS GOOD.

AT DAWN WE SIGHTED THE **FLYING SUB**, WALLOWING ALONG ABOUT A THOUSAND FEET BELOW US—

BUT WHY DIDN'T SHE **HEAVE TO** AND STAND-BY AS I **ORDERED** HER BY RADIO?

IT DOES SEEM TO **OOFAH** OF HER — B-BUT LET'S SEE WHAT SHE HAS TO SAY.

WHILE ON THE FLYING SUBMARINE, ARDALA VALMAR STUDIED OUR FLYABOUT WITH SATISFACTION —

SO THAT'S THE FAMOUS **BUCK ROGERS!** GOOD I GOT RID OF — OF MY PASSENGER IN TIME — WELL, LET 'EM COME ABOARD! — I'VE GOT A GOOD STORY TO TELL.

TO BE CONTINUED
591.

WILMA AND I FINALLY OVERTOOK OUR **FLYING SUBMARINE**, WHICH HAD SO STRANGELY HOPPED OFF WITHOUT US, UNDER THE COMMAND OF THIRD OFFICER ARDALA VALMAR.

COPYRIGHT JOHN F. DILLE CO. REG. U.S. PAT. OFF.

WILMA NEATLY LANDED THE **Q-RAY** FLYABOUT ON THE DECK OF THE **FLYING SUBMARINE.**

GIVE HER A CHANCE, BUCK—SEE WHAT SHE HAS TO SAY.

OH— I'LL GIVE HER A CHANCE ALL RIGHT, BUT IF SHE HASN'T A PRETTY CLICKY STORY—

BOAT CREW ON DECK! STOW THE COMMANDER'S FLYABOUT BELOW

I LOST NO TIME IN QUESTIONING LIEUTENANT VALMAR.

COMMANDER ROGERS—THIS IS LT VALMAR—.

OH— HOW ARE YOU, VALMAR— AND WHAT'S THE IDEA OF MAKING OFF WITH THIS SHIP?

YOUR OWN ORDERS, SIR!

BUT I SENT YOU NO ORDERS!!

HIS OWN ORDERS??

UNDOUBTEDLY IF THE COMMANDER **SAYS** SO — BUT OUR **RADIO-OPERATOR** RECEIVED ORDERS PURPORTING TO COME FROM HIM!

TO BE CONTINUED
592

WILMA AND I AT LAST WERE ABOARD OUR **FLYING SUBMARINE** WITH WHICH WE WERE TO SEARCH FOR THE **SUNKEN CITY** OF **ATLANTIS**, WITH ITS **LIVING INHABITANTS**, SOME OF WHOM HAD SECRETLY VISITED OUR AMERICAN CITIES. THIRD OFFICER ARDALA VALMAR HAD OFFERED A PLAUSIBLE EXPLANATION FOR EMBARKING WITHOUT US—.

COPYRIGHT JOHN F. DILLE CO REG. U.S. PAT. OFF.

THE RADIO RECORD DID INDEED SHOW AN ORDER PURPORTING TO COME FROM ME!

THEN THE COMMANDER IS SATISFIED I DID MY DUTY?

HMM! ER- YES I GUESS YOU COULDN'T HAVE DONE ANYTHING ELSE.

THERE'S SOMETHING FISHY IN THIS BUSINESS — AND YET—

WILMA TOOK THE NEXT WATCH.

SET YOUR COURSE FOR THE **AZORES**— I'M GOING **BELOW** AND TURN IN.

ALL CLICKY, BUCK DEAR— I — I MEAN AYE—AYE—SIR!

AFTER I HAD GONE BELOW, THE MAN AT THE HELM SPOKE TO WILMA—.

I HADN'T RIGHTLY OUGHT TO REPORT NOTHING ABOUT AN **OFFICER**, MISS—BUT I SEEN LT. VALMAR PULL A FUNNY ONE—

WHAT? WHAT DID SHE DO?

TO BE CONTINUED
593

ABOARD OUR **FLYING SUBMARINE** WITH WHICH WE WERE TO EXPLORE THE **LOST ATLANTIS**—ARDALA VALMAR, THIRD OFFICER, HAD GIVEN A **PLAUSIBLE EXCUSE** FOR SEEMING TO RUN AWAY WITH THE SHIP— WE WERE CRUISING 1,000 FEET ABOVE THE SURFACE THE STEERSMAN HAD BEGUN TO SPIN A YARN OF SUSPICION ABOUT ARDALA TO WILMA, WHEN—

COPYRIGHT JOHN F. DILLE CO. REG. U.S. PAT. OFF.

A CRY FOR ALARM RANG THROUGH THE VESSEL!

MAN OVERBOARD!

HUH?

DOWN—DOWN—CIRCLE LEFT AND DIVE! ALL HANDS TO STATIONS! CLOSE HATCHES!

AS WE PLUNGED HEAVILY DOWNWARD —

???

WE PLUNGED — THEN LUNGED TO THE SURFACE!

WHO IS IT?

A GIRL— A STRANGE GIRL— WITHOUT ANY— ER — AH BATHING SUIT—!

BUT WHERE IS SHE?

TO BE CONTINUED
594

SUNKEN CITY OF ATLANTIS

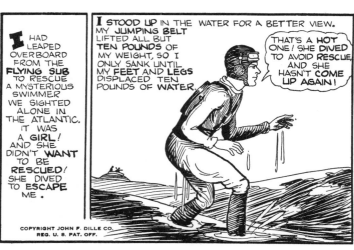

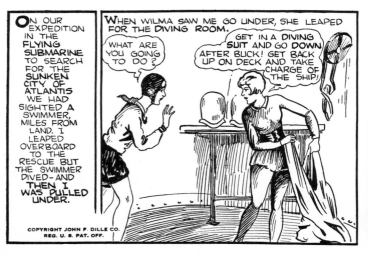

Row 1

I HAD BEEN PULLED UNDER THE WATER WHEN I LEAPED OVERBOARD FROM THE **FLYING SUBMARINE** TO RESCUE THE MYSTERIOUS SWIMMER. I FOUND MYSELF THE PRISONER OF "MERMAIDS"— GIRLS WHO COULD EITHER BREATHE WATER, OR LIKE SEALS AND WHALES, GO A LONG TIME WITHOUT BREATHING AIR—.

COPYRIGHT JOHN F. DILLE CO.
REG. U. S. PAT. OFF.

I WAS ALMOST UNCONSCIOUS WHEN MY CAPTORS SAW WILMA PLUNGING DOWN FROM ABOVE TO THE RESCUE.

???
?

THEY RELEASED ME IN THEIR FRIGHT—MY JUMPING BELT CARRIED ME UPWARD LIKE A ROCKET!

BUCK!

PLOP!

I WAS UNCONSCIOUS WHEN WE REACHED THE SURFACE, MY **JUMPING BELT** LIFTING ALL BUT MY FEET ABOVE THE WATER.

WHAT'S THE MATTER WITH ARDALA? SHE COULD SEE US EASILY— BUT— SHE WON'T LOOK THIS WAY!! SUFFERING ROCKETS! DOES SHE REALLY WANT TO LOSE US?

TO BE CONTINUED
599

Row 2

WILMA HAD RESCUED ME FROM THE STRANGE "OCEAN GIRLS" WHO HAD PULLED ME UNDER—BUT **NOW** IT LOOKED AS THOUGH ARDALA, WHOM SHE HAD LEFT IN COMMAND OF THE FLYING SUBMARINE, DID NOT **WANT** TO SEE US AND HAUL US ABOARD.

COPYRIGHT JOHN F. DILLE CO.
REG. U. S. PAT. OFF.

BUT A MEMBER OF THE CREW SAW US, AND REPORTED TO HER.

THERE THEY ARE, LIEUTENANT! THEY'VE COME UP!

HUH! WH-WHAT?— WHERE?

BY THE TIME THEY HAULED ME ABOARD I HAD RECOVERED CONSCIOUSNESS—.

I WAS LOOKING **ALL OVER** FOR YOU, AND DIDN'T SEE YOU ANYWHERE!

OH— YOU DIDN'T— DIDN'T YOU?

ALL HANDS BELOW!-CLOSE HATCHES! PREPARE TO SUBMERGE— WE'RE GOING **DOWN** AFTER THOSE UNDER-WATER PEOPLE!

INTO THE DEPTHS WE PLUNGED—LITTLE REALIZING WHAT LAY BEFORE US!

TO BE CONT:NUED
600

Row 3

WE PLUNGED INTO THE DEPTHS, SEEKING SOME SIGN OF ATLANTIS, THE ANCIENT CITY THAT SANK BENEATH THE OCEAN.

COPYRIGHT JOHN F. DILLE CO.
REG. U. S. PAT. OFF.

I WAS SUSPICIOUS OF ARDALA VALMAR. I TOLD WILMA SO—.

SHE TRIED TO **STEAL** THIS SHIP— BUT WE CAN'T PROVE IT.

AND SHE TRIED TO ABANDON US WHEN WE WENT OVERBOARD.

AT THE SAME MOMENT ARDALA, IN THE PRIVACY OF HER CABIN———

BUCK AND WILMA ARE BEGINNING TO **SUSPECT** ME—I'LL HAVE TO GIVE THEM SOMETHING ELSE TO **THINK** ABOUT!

AND SO—LATER—WHEN ARDALA ENTERED THE CHART ROOM——

THIS IS HIGHLY IRREGULAR! WHERE IS YOUR UNIFORM?

IN MY CABIN OF COURSE-I DON'T HAVE TO WEAR IT, DO I, WHEN I'M NOT ON DUTY?

SHE THINKS SHE'LL VAMP MY BUCK AWAY FROM ME, DOES SHE? WELL— I'LL SEE ABOUT THAT!

TO BE CONTINUED
601

Row 4

OUR CRAFT DRIFTED ON OVER A SUBMARINE PLAIN IN SEARCH OF ATLANTIS. ARDALA VALMAR, OUR THIRD OFFICER, HAD EMBARRASSED ME BY APPEARING WITHOUT HER UNIFORM.

COPYRIGHT JOHN F. DILLE CO.
REG. U. S. PAT. OFF.

I DIDN'T LIKE TO GIVE ARDALA A CALL-DOWN IN FRONT OF WILMA.

NO, THERE IS NOTHING IN THE REGULATIONS ABOUT HOW YOU DRESS WHEN OFF DUTY—

WELL!— IF BUCK LIKES THEM TO DRESS LIKE THAT! I'LL MAKE ARDALA LOOK LIKE A RAG DOLL!

YOU MUSN'T HURRY OUT ON MY ACCOUNT, WILMA.

BUT AS SOON AS WILMA LEFT THE CHART ROOM—

YOUR NOT GOING TO BE MEAN TO ME, ARE YOU—BUCK?

YOU FORGOT YOUR-SELF, REMEMBER, LIEUTENANT VALMAR, THAT I'M CAPTAIN ROGERS TO YOU! AND FURTHERMORE—

AT LAST ARDALA REALIZED I MEANT IT. I DIDN'T SEE WILMA ENTER.

I BEG THE CAPTAIN'S PARDON. THE CAPTAIN'S ORDERS SHALL BE OBEYED.

AND IF ANY OFFICER APPEARS OUT OF UNIFORM SHE WILL BE PLACED UNDER ARREST!

??

TO BE CONTINUED
602

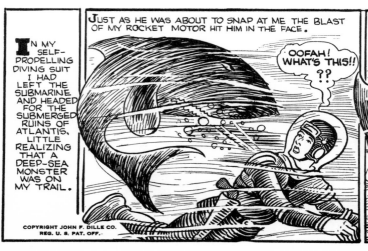

NO SOONER HAD I LEFT OUR SUBMERGED CRAFT TO EXPLORE THE SUNKEN RUINS OF ATLANTIS, THAN I WAS ATTACKED BY A HUGE SHARK. ONLY THE ROCKET MOTOR OF MY DIVING SUIT SAVED ME.

I STREAKED FOR ONE OF THE SUBMERGED BUILDINGS.

I'LL SLIDE IN THIS PORT — I'M FISH-BAIT IF I DON'T MAKE IT!

PUT-PUT

BUT I MADE IT— AND SHOT THROUGH INTO THE INKY BLACKNESS BEYOND.

THAT WAS A NARROW SQUEAK!

I FOUND MYSELF IN A ROOM FULL OF STRANGE MACHINERY. THE SHARK COULDN'T GET THROUGH THE ENTRANCE.

CORAL FORMATIONS HAVE GROWN OVER EVERYTHING! THIS PLACE HAS BEEN ABANDON'ED FOR CENTURIES! YET THAT MACHINE LOOKS MODERN!

TO BE CONTINUED 607.

CHASED BY A SHARK INTO ONE OF THE SUBMERGED RUINS OF ANCIENT ATLANTIS, I FOUND A MARVELOUS MACHINE. IT WAS ENCRUSTED WITH CORAL, AND MUST HAVE BEEN ABANDONED OVER 1,000 YEARS BEFORE.

AS I THOUGHT! THE CORAL CRUMBLES AWAY EASILY!—LET'S SEE WHAT THIS GADGET LOOKS LIKE!

LOOKS SOMETHING LIKE AN ATOMIC DISINTEGRATOR- BUT IT'S THOUSANDS OF YEARS OLD—NOW I WONDER—

SUDDENLY, AT MY TOUCH, BRILLIANT LIGHTS GLOWED IN STRANGE-SHAPED TUBES, AND THE ANCIENT- APPARATUS WENT INTO ACTION-

WHAT THE-?

TO BE CONTINUED 608.

AFTER ESCAPING A SHARK I WAS EXPLORING A RUIN OF ANCIENT ATLANTIS, THE CITY THAT SANK BENEATH THE OCEAN. I CAME UPON A MARVELOUS MACHINE, THOUSANDS OF YEARS OLD AT MY TOUCH STRANGE TUBES GLOWED AND PULSED, AND OMINOUS SOUNDS CAME FROM THE INTERIOR OF THE APPARATUS.

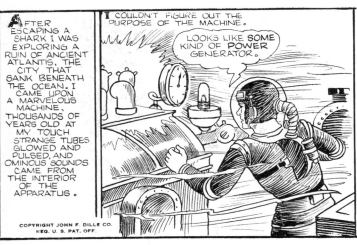

I COULDN'T FIGURE OUT THE PURPOSE OF THE MACHINE.

LOOKS LIKE SOME KIND OF POWER GENERATOR.

WITHOUT WARNING THERE CAME A TERRIBLE SURGE IN THE WATER IN THE ROOM.

WHOA! WHOA! IT'S SWEEPING ME OUT TOWARD THAT SHARK I DODGED!

WITH A TERRIBLE SWEEP, THE WATER RUSHED OUT THE DOOR I HAD ENTERED.

OOFAH! IT'S TEARING ME LOOSE! I CAN'T HOLD ON— MUCH-LONGER!

TO BE CONT-NUED 609.

I HAD LEFT OUR SUBMERGED CRAFT TO EXPLORE THE RUINS OF ATLANTIS— IN AN ANCIENT BUILDING FOUND A STRANGE MACHINE— SUDDENLY IT WENT INTO ACTION A TERRIFIC CURRENT OF WATER TORE AT ME— I HELD ON DESPERATELY.

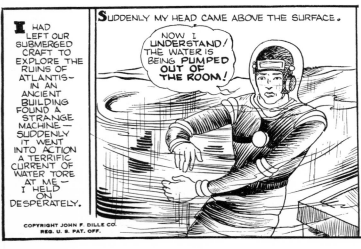

SUDDENLY MY HEAD CAME ABOVE THE SURFACE.

NOW I UNDERSTAND! THE WATER IS BEING PUMPED OUT OF THE ROOM!

SOME MYSTERIOUS FORCE KEPT THE SOLID WALL OF SEA-WATER FROM POURING BACK INTO THE ROOM.

NOW WHAT'S HOLDING THAT WATER BACK?! CAN THERE BE A KIND OF MAGNETISM THAT ACTS ON WATER?

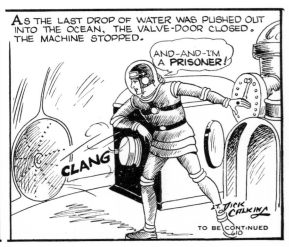

AS THE LAST DROP OF WATER WAS PUSHED OUT INTO THE OCEAN, THE VALVE-DOOR CLOSED. THE MACHINE STOPPED.

AND-AND-I'M A PRISONER!

CLANG

TO BE CONTINUED 610.

SUNKEN CITY OF ATLANTIS

BUCK ROGERS IN THE 25th CENTURY

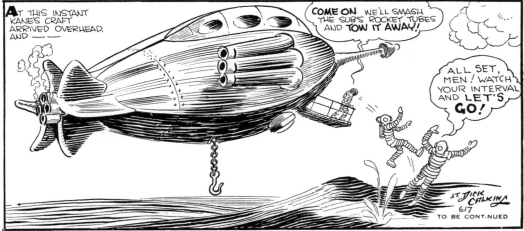

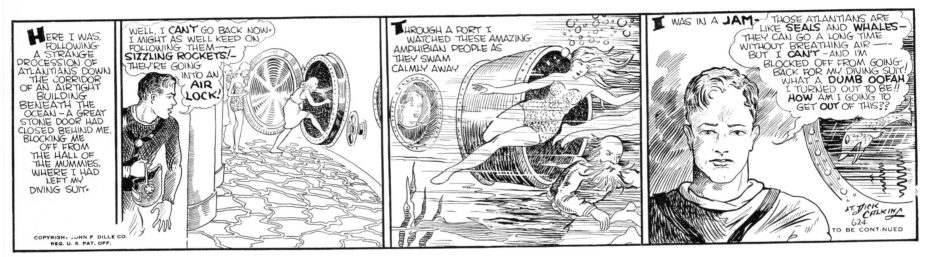

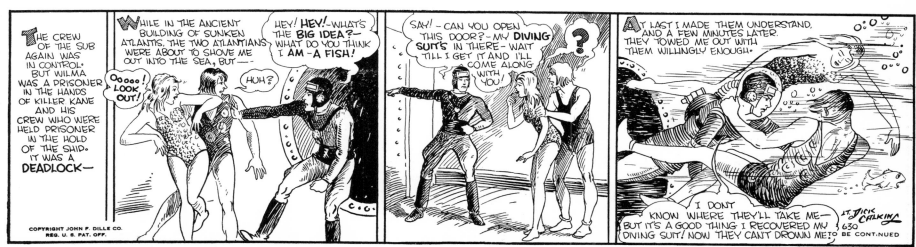

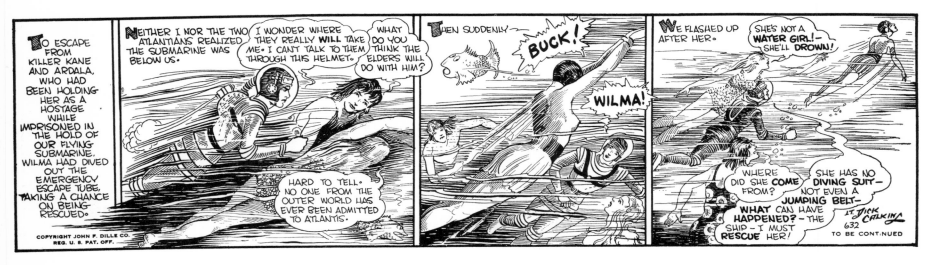

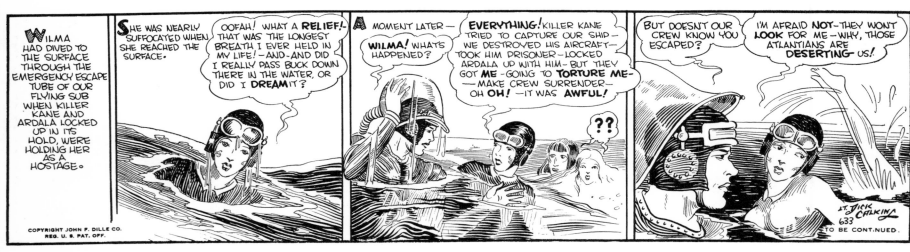

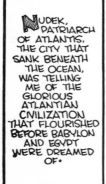

SUNKEN CITY OF ATLANTIS

NUDEK, PATRIARCH OF ATLANTIS TOLD US THAT ONCE — 50,000 YEARS BEFORE — A CONTINENT HAD STRETCHED FROM THE WEST INDIES TO EUROPE • HE CONTINUED —

IN THE YEAR 47,270 B•C• A TIDAL WAVE SWEPT DOWN OVER WEST ATLANTIS. THE LAND DISAPPEARED FOREVER•

COPYRIGHT JOHN F. DILLE CO.
REG. U. S. PAT. OFF.

THE SURVIVORS' WESTWARD OF THE CATACLYSM FLED TO THE TROPICAL HIGHLANDS KNOWN AS YUCATAN•

THERE THEY FOUNDED A CIVILIZATION LONG SINCE FORGOTTEN — THIS EXPLAINS THE MAYA AND INCA LEGENDS OF AN ANCIENT GOLDEN-HAIRED RACE•

BUT WHAT OF THE ATLANTIANS **EAST** OF THE GREAT FLOOD?

LT. DICK CALKINS
643
TO BE CONTINUED

NUDEK, PATRIARCH OF ATLANTIS, CONTINUED HIS NARRATIVE — AS WE JOINED WILMA IN THE LIBRARY —

BUT WHAT OF ATLANTIS **ITSELF**?

WAS **IT** SUBMERGED **IMMEDIATELY**?

NO-OO NOT EXACTLY —

COPYRIGHT JOHN F. DILLE CO.
REG. U. S. PAT. OFF.

EAST OF ATLANTIS — CENTURY BY CENTURY — THE LAND SANK — BUT GREAT **DYKES** HELD BACK THE SEA•

FOR 17,000 YEARS THE ATLANTIANS WAGED WAR AGAINST THE SEA — BUT IN THE END — IN 30,000 B•C• —

FLY! FLY! — THE WALL IS **CRACKING**! — AND WE'RE 800 FEET **BELOW** SEA LEVEL!

LT. DICK CALKINS
644
TO BE CONT•NUED

— THE EAST ATLANTIANS WHO ESCAPED THE GREAT FLOOD MARCHED THROUGH SOUTHERN EUROPE TOWARD SCYTHIA•

NUDEK CONTINUED HIS NARRATION OF HISTORY LONG SINCE FORGOTTEN, EXCEPT IN ATLANTIS BENEATH THE SEA.

COPYRIGHT JOHN F. DILLE CO.
REG. U. S. PAT. OFF.

— SOME OF THEM STOPPED AT THE SHORES OF THE MEDITERRANEAN SEA — PRESERVING A REMNANT OF THE ANCIENT ATLANTIAN CULTURE• THEY WERE KNOWN 20,000 YEARS LATER AS THE GREEKS•

SO **THAT'S** WHERE THE ANCIENT GREEKS CAME FROM!

BUT HOW ABOUT **YOU** ATLANTIANS — LIVING HERE **UNDER THE SEA** — SWIMMING ABOUT FOR HOURS **WITHOUT BREATHING**?

I'M **COMING** TO THAT —

LT. DICK CALKINS
645
TO BE CONT•NUED

NUDEK CONTINUED ———

BUT WHAT ABOUT ATLANTIS WHEN IT SANK BENEATH THE OCEAN?

— BUT UNDER ATLANTIS ITSELF, ENGINEERS HAD FOUND VAST CAVERNS WITH AN UNLIMITED SUPPLY OF AIR — BUILDINGS WERE MADE WATER-TIGHT BEFORE THE SEA SWEPT OVER THEM.

COPYRIGHT JOHN F. DILLE CO.
REG. U. S. PAT. OFF.

— AS THOUSANDS OF YEARS PASSED, ATLANTIANS LEARNED TO SWIM FOR LONG PERIODS WITHOUT BREATHING — LIKE SEA MAMMALS THEY WERE AT HOME IN EITHER WATER OR AIR•

— IN 15,368 B•C• AN EXPEDITION LEFT ATLANTIS TO COLONIZE THE UPPER WORLD.

A STRANGE DESTINY AWAITED IT!

LT. DICK CALKINS
646
TO BE CONT•NUED

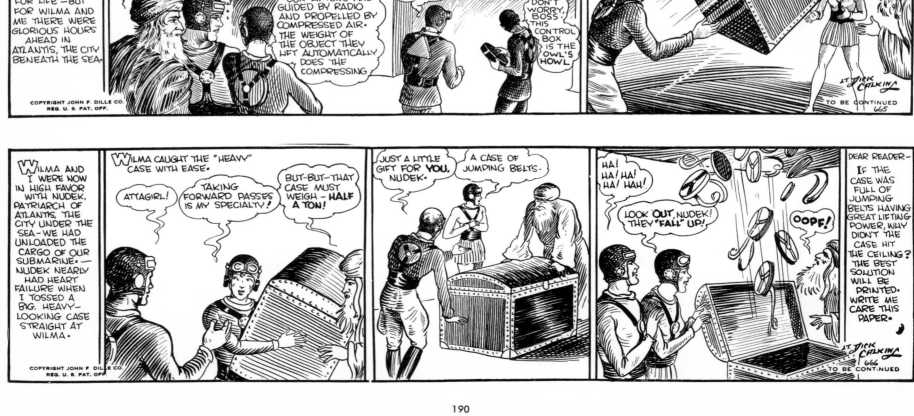

SUNKEN CITY OF ATLANTIS

SUNKEN CITY OF ATLANTIS

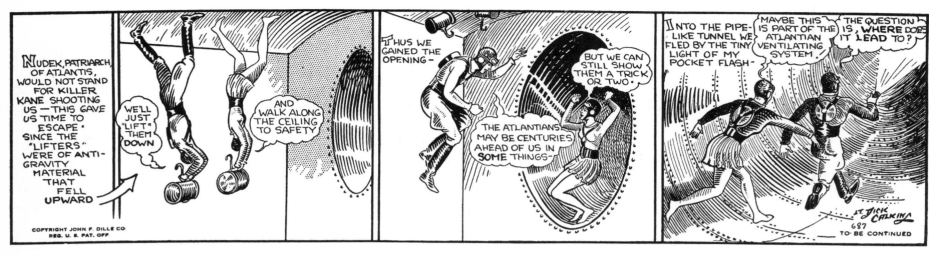

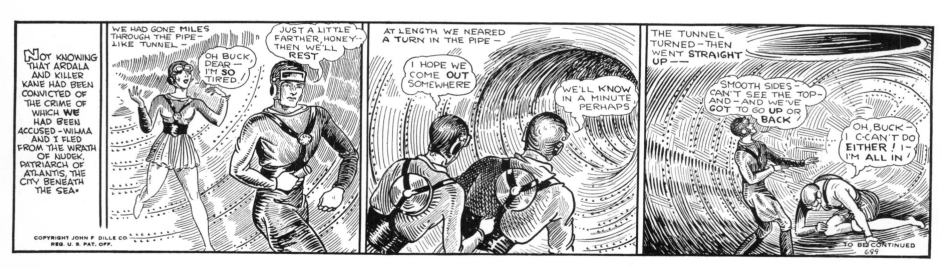

SUNKEN CITY OF ATLANTIS

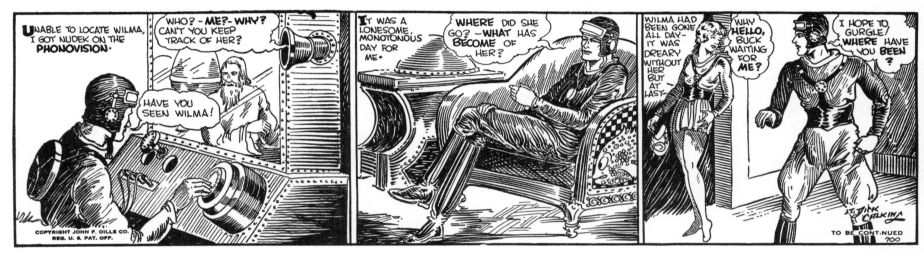

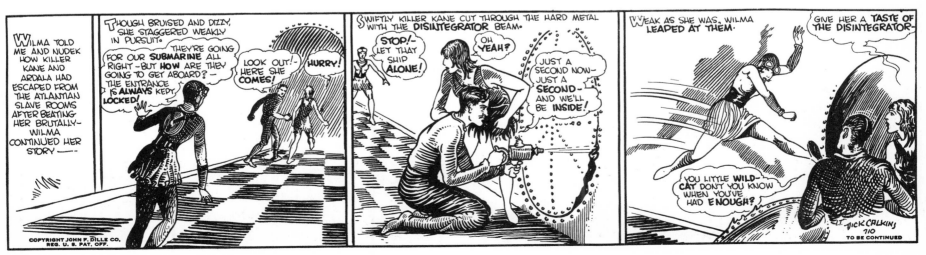

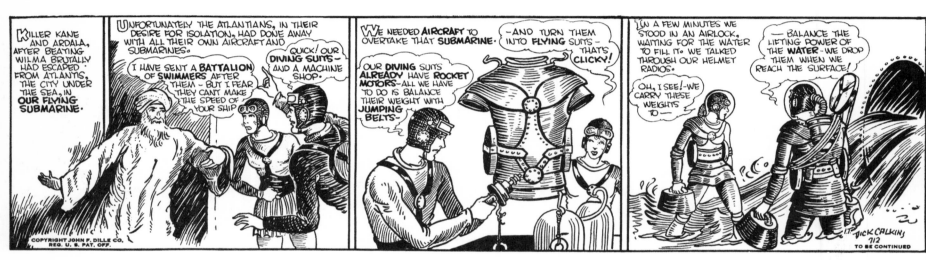

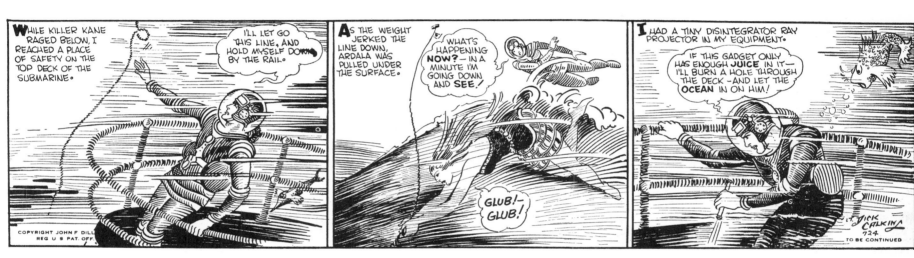

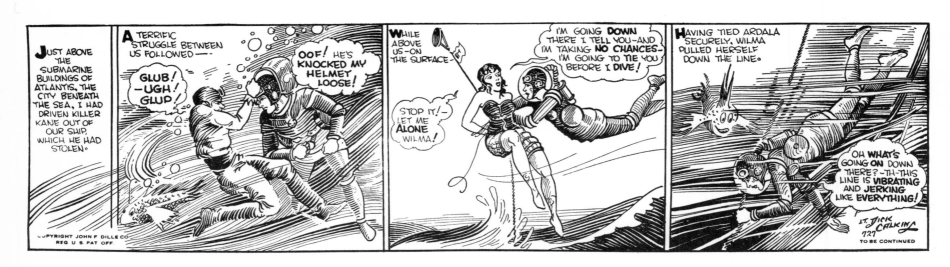

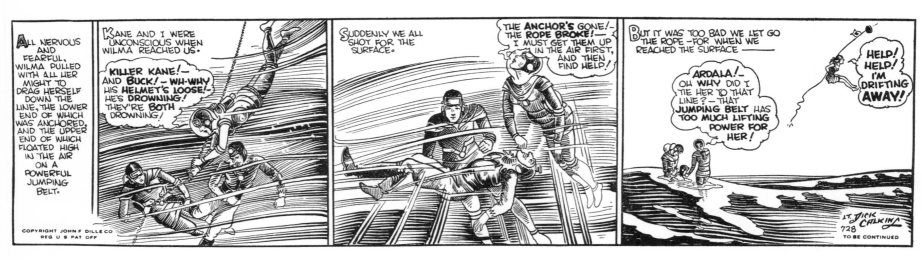

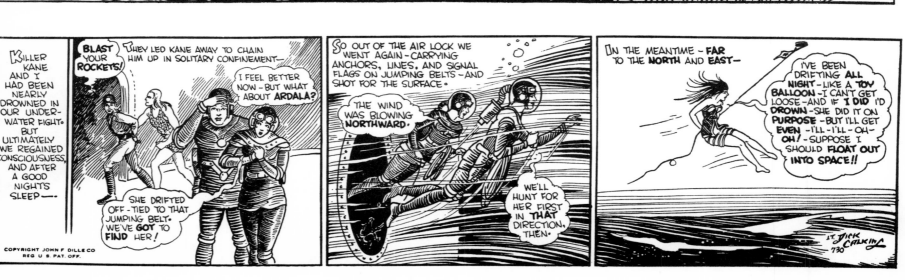

7
MYSTERY OF ATLANTIAN GOLD SHIPS

MYSTERY OF ATLANTIAN GOLD SHIPS

NOT KNOWING THAT ARDALA HAD BEEN RESCUED BY BLACK BARNEY AND HIS AIR-PIRATE CREW — NOR THAT SHE WIELDED A STRANGE INFLUENCE OVER HIM, WILMA AND I SET SAIL FROM ATLANTIS, IN OUR FLYING SUBMARINE, BEARING THE TREATY THAT WOULD OPEN UP ATLANTIS TO WORLD TRADE.

COPYRIGHT JOHN F DILLE CO
REG U S PAT OFF

WHEN WE HAD FORGED SOME DISTANCE FROM THE SUNKEN CITY, WE LUNGED UP FROM THE DEPTHS INTO THE AIR FOR GREATER SPEED.

AT 30,000 FEET WE LEVELLED OFF AND FLASHED FOR HOME UNDER FULL ROCKET POWER.

BUT FAR ABOVE NIAGARA — IN BLACK BARNEY'S PIRATE CRUISER. THE CHIEF IS ON A FISHING TRIP — HE LEFT STRICT ORDERS TO BOTHER HIM WITH NO OFFICIAL BUSINESS.

ARDALA! — LISTEN TO THIS NEWS FLASH!

CLICKY! — WHAT A BREAK! — WHILE BUCKS IS WAITING FOR THE CHIEF TO RETURN, I'LL GET A COPY OF THAT TREATY!

DICK CALKINS 735
TO BE CONTINUED

WILMA AND I WERE FLASHING ON FROM ATLANTIS TO AMERICA WITH THE TREATY WHICH WOULD OPEN UP THE CITY BENEATH THE SEA TO WORLD TRADE — BUT A MYSTERY SHIP HAD ARRIVED BEFORE US — BEYOND THE RANGE OF DETECTOSCOPES, IT HUNG AN INVISIBLE SPECK, HIGH IN THE STRATOSPHERE.

COPYRIGHT JOHN F DILLE CO
REG U S. PAT. OFF.

ABOARD THIS CRAFT — NEAR ONE OF ITS AIR-LOCKS — LISTEN, ARDALA — YOU CAN'T STEP OFF HERE — THERE ISN'T A POUND OF AIR PRESSURE OUTSIDE.

STOP YAMMERING, I'LL BE ALL RIGHT — I'LL TAKE A SPACE SUIT AND AN AIR-JIT — I'VE GOT TO GET A COPY OF THAT TREATY!

A MOMENT LATER A TRAP POPPED OPEN AND A TINY CRAFT PLUNGED FROM IT LIKE A STONE.

BUT THE TINY CRAFT WAS NOT BUILT FOR OPERATION IN THE NEAR-VACCUUM OF THE STRATOSPHERE — IT PLUNGED WITH TERRIFIC ACCELERATION.

I DON'T LIKE THIS AT ALL! — WHEN I DO HIT THE ATMOSPHERE THE AIR FRICTION IS GOING TO BE AWFUL!

AT LAST DOWN INTO DENSER AIR.

IT'S GETTING RED HOT! IF I DON'T CHECK THIS SPEED THE SHIP WILL MELT!!

DICK CALKINS 736
TO BE CONTINUED

ARDALA HAD DROPPED DOWN OVER THE CAPITAL, FROM THE PIRATE CRAFT OF BLACK BARNEY, TO LAY PLANS TO STEAL A COPY OF THE TREATY I WAS BRINGING FROM ATLANTIS, WHICH WOULD OPEN UP TO THE WORLD THE SUNKEN CITY.

THROWING OUT AN "AIR-ANCHOR" ARDALA MANAGED TO CHECK THE TERRIBLE, PLUNGING SPEED OF HER TINY CRAFT.

COPYRIGHT JOHN F DILLE CO
REG U S PAT OFF

PHOOIE! — WHAT A DROP THAT WAS! — FOR A MOMENT I THOUGHT THE AIR FRICTION WOULD BURN ME UP — LET'S SEE NOW — YES, THIS IS THE PLACE — AND NOT A SHIP IN SIGHT FOR MILES.

AND THEN — OFF WITH THAT SPACE SUIT — AND NOW TO SLIP INTO SOMETHING CHIC AND PRETTY — 'CAUSE I'VE GOT SOME TALL VAMPING TO DO.

THEN SHE HEADED FOR ONE OF THOSE AIR-HOUSES THAT HAD REPLACED THE ROAD-HOUSES OF AN EARLIER DAY.

THAT'S IT — THE ROOST — EDDIE LAFFOX USED TO HANG OUT THERE — NOW, IF MY LUCK ONLY HOLDS OUT —

DICK CALKINS 737
TO BE CONTINUED

WILMA AND I WERE ROCKETING — FULL BLAST FOR NIAGARA, BUT ARDALA, HAVING JOINED FORCES WITH BLACK BARNEY, THE AIR-PIRATE — ALREADY WAS LAYING PLANS TO STEAL A COPY OF THE ATLANTIAN TREATY, MOORING HER AIR-JIT TO A STANCHION, SHE ENTERED A FLOATING INN CALLED THE ROOST, WHERE —

COPYRIGHT JOHN F DILLE CO
REG. U. S. PAT. OFF.

EDDIE LAFFOX! OF ALL PEOPLE! ARE YOU STILL SECRETARY TO THE CHIEF EXECUTIVE?

ARDALA! IS IT REALLY YOU? OH — WHY, YES — I GUESS I AM — — —

AFTER LUNCHEON, IN THE FLOATING GARDEN —

LISTEN, EDDIE — I'LL GIVE YOU FIFTY GRAND FOR A PHOTOSTAT OF THE ATLANTIAN TREATY. THAT UNDERWATER HICK TOWN IS FULL OF GOLD!

NO — NO — I COULDN'T! THAT WOULD BE TREASON! OH, ARDALA — NOT THAT!

WHY — EDDIE! YOU USED TO LOVE ME! OH, HOW MANY NIGHTS I'VE CRIED MYSELF TO SLEEP! I'LL — I'LL MARRY YOU, EDDIE. — AND TOGETHER — JUST YOU AND I —

STOP! DON'T TEMPT ME FURTHER! — MY DUTY! — I'LL BE A TRAITOR! — BUT — I CAN'T RESIST YOU — I'LL — I'LL GIVE YOU A COPY OF THE TREATY — BUT IF I'M CAUGHT — THE COUNCIL IS MERCILESS!

DICK CALKINS 738
TO BE CONTINUED

MYSTERY OF ATLANTIAN GOLD SHIPS

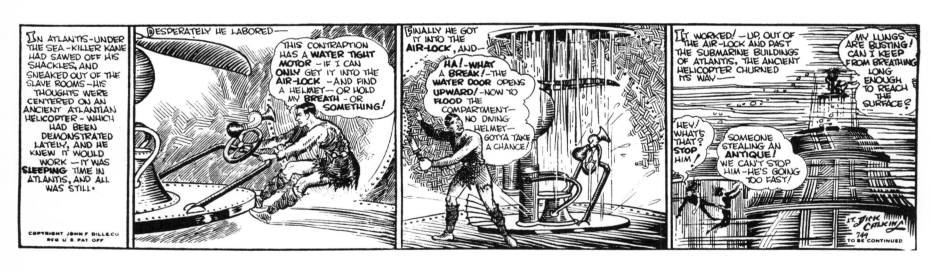

MYSTERY OF ATLANTIAN GOLD SHIPS

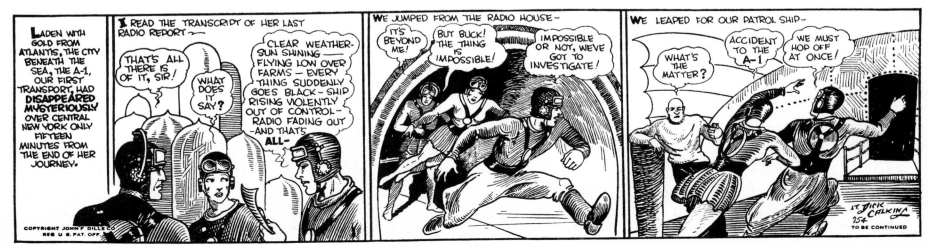

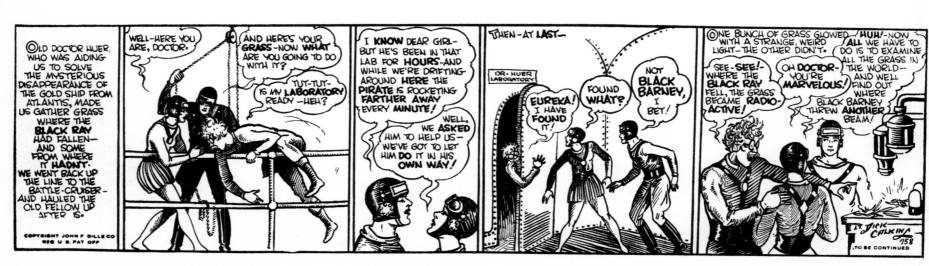

MYSTERY OF ATLANTIAN GOLD SHIPS

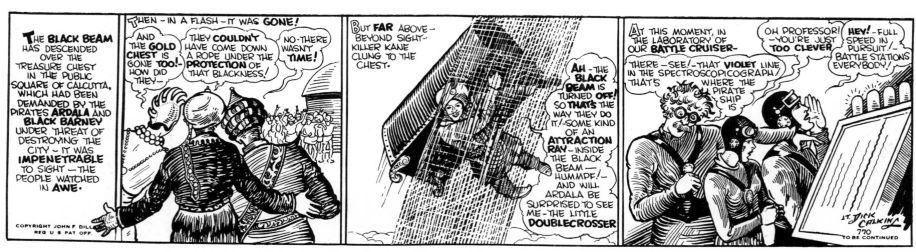

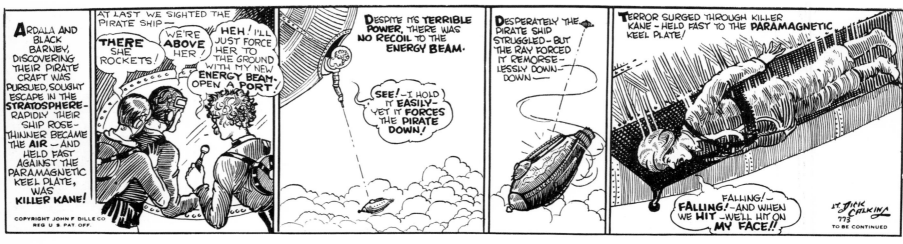

MYSTERY OF ATLANTIAN GOLD SHIPS

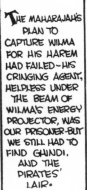

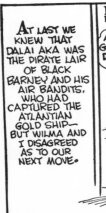

8
MARTIAN WAR THREAT

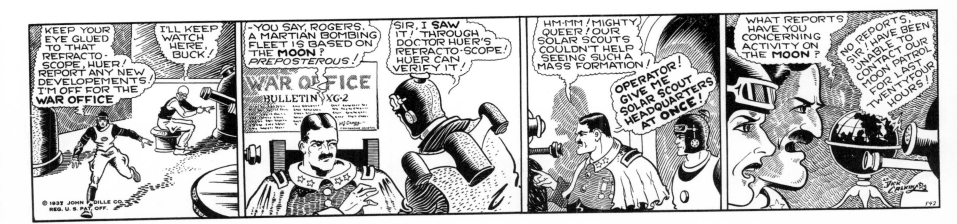

MARTIAN WAR THREAT

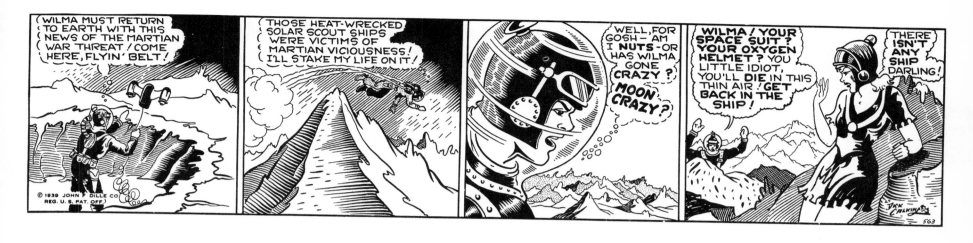

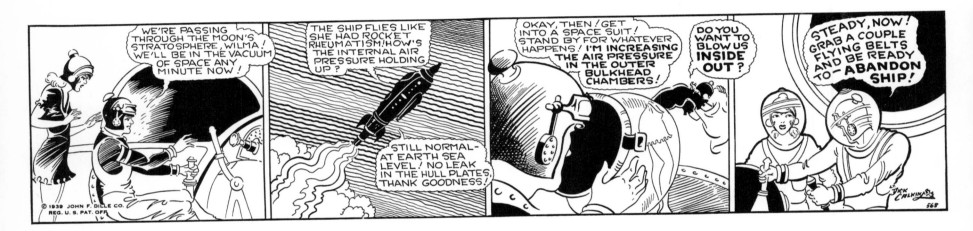

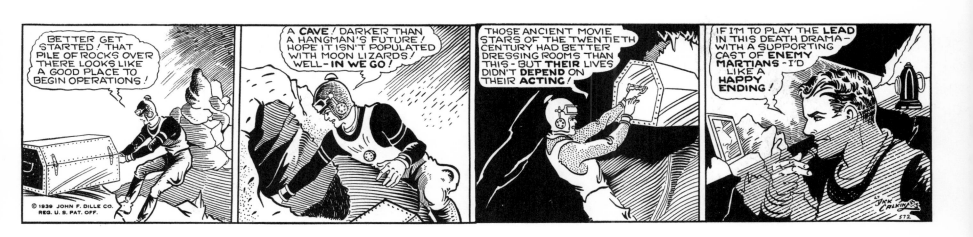

MARTIAN WAR THREAT

MARTIAN WAR THREAT

BUCK ROGERS IN THE 25th CENTURY

MARTIAN WAR THREAT

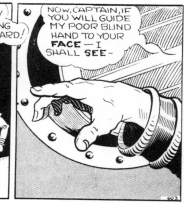

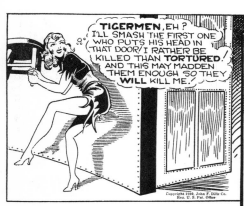

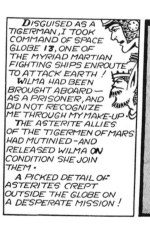

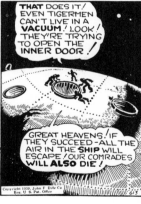

BUCK ROGERS IN THE 25th CENTURY

MARTIAN WAR THREAT

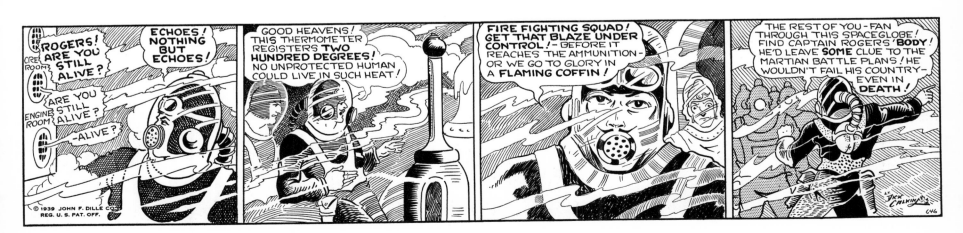

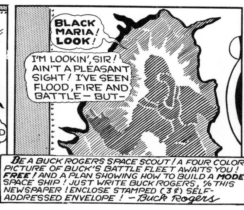

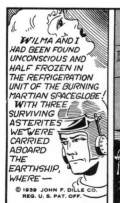

ABOARD THE EARTHSHIP, WILMA AND I – WITH THREE SURVIVING ASTERITES – HOVER BETWEEN LIFE AND DEATH FROM OUR TERRIBLE EXPERIENCE ON THE MARTIAN GLOBESHIP! WITH THE SPACEGLOBE IN TOW, THE SCOUTSHIP HEADS FOR EARTH WHEN A COSMIC HURRICANE THREATENS IT!

MORE SPEED! MORE SPEED!

CAN'T MAKE IT, SIR! TOO MUCH DRAG ASTERN!

THEN CUT LOOSE THAT MARTIAN HULK! CAN'T RACE A COSMIC HURRICANE WITH DEADWEIGHT TIED TO OUR TAIL!

AYE, SIR!

HELLO! EMERGENCY SQUAD! DISINTEGRATE THAT TOW CABLE! JUMP!

SHE'S FREE SIR!

GOOD! HOLD YOUR COURSE AND USE FULL POWER!

THE DESERTED SPACEGLOBE, LEFT TO THE FURY OF THE COSMIC STORM, PLUNGED LIKE A MADDENED BEAST!

BUT WAIT! WAS THE GLOBESHIP ENTIRELY DESERTED? HAS EVERY ONE BEEN ACCOUNTED FOR?

GOOD THING WE CUT LOOSE FROM THAT SPACE GLOBE WHEN WE DID! WE'D NEVER HAVE COME THROUGH THAT COSMIC STORM ALIVE!

RIGHT, SIR! WE'D BE A TWISTED WRECK BY NOW!

SIR! CAPTAIN ROGERS IS CONSCIOUS AND ASKING FOR YOU!

CONSCIOUS? GOOD! EARTH CAN'T AFFORD TO LOSE HIM!

WILMA'S SAFE, CAPTAIN PICKETT? THANK HEAVENS!

AND THREE ASTERITES ALSO?

THE OTHERS WERE DEAD, ROGERS! WE GAVE THEM A SPACE BURIAL – WITH FULL MILITARY HONORS!

WE CUT THE GLOBESHIP ADRIFT! HAD TO! GOT CAUGHT IN A COSMIC FORCE STORM –

BUT WHAT BECAME OF THAT BLIND SPY?

WHAT BECAME OF WHAT BLIND SPY?

WING BAT WU! INFORMER! AGITATOR! MARTIAN SECRET AGENT! HE WAS LOCKED UP ABOARD THAT SPACEGLOBE! IN THE BRIG!

THE ONE PLACE WE DIDN'T SEARCH! I'D GIVE MY RIGHT ARM TO LAY HANDS ON THAT HEEL! HE'S DEAD BY NOW, THOUGH!

DEAD OR ALIVE – WE'VE GOT TO FIND HIM! WE'VE GOT TO!

WING BAT WU HOLDS THE WAR SECRETS OF THE MARTIAN ATTACK!

MEANTIME – IN THE DERELICT SPACEGLOBE –

WHERE AM I? WHAT HAPPENED? BLAST MY EYES, I'VE BEEN DEAD TO THE WORLD!

NO MOTOR VIBRATION! NO MOTION! I SENSE DISASTER!

THIS GHASTLY SILENCE IS DRIVING ME MAD! MAD! MAD – I SAY! LOCKED IN THE PRISON CELL OF THIS BLASTED GLOBESHIP!

WHY, BURN ME IF I'D TREAT A DOG THIS WAY! WHY DOESN'T SOMEONE COME?

HEY!

HEY! HEY! HEY! HEY!

HEY! HEY!

HEY! HEY! HEY! HEY!

ECHOES! MOCKING ME! THEY CAN'T DO THIS TO WING BAT WU! OH, MY POOR UNSEEING EYES!

THE DOOR! IT'S BEEN SPRUNG LOOSE! NOW I'LL – BUT HUSH, IT MAY BE THAT ROGERS HAS SET A SNARE FOR ME!

IF SO, HE'LL FIND HE'S CAUGHT A SOLAR MONSTER!

MARTIAN WAR THREAT

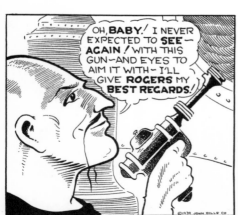

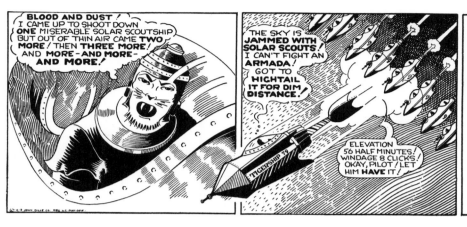

MARTIAN WAR THREAT

BUCK ROGERS IN THE 25th CENTURY

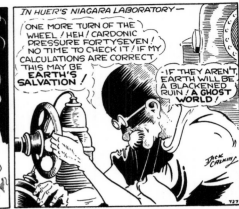

9
MARTIANS INVADE JUPITER

BUCK ROGERS
IN THE 25th CENTURY

THE MAIN BATTLE MUST BE AN **INFERNO** BY NOW! MY SQUADRON IS OUTNUMBERED TWO TO ONE! GOT TO GET IN THERE AND **FIGHT!**

WHEW! FROM THE LOOKS OF THOSE WRECKED MARTIAN SHIPS, MY ROCKET RANGERS HAVE DONE A **JOB!**

FLIGHT LEADER NUMBER NINE, REPORTING! ENEMY SPACE CRAFT TOTALLY **DESTROYED!**

GREAT WORK, RANGERS! YOUR COUNTRY WILL BE GRATEFUL! PROCEED WITH CONVOY TO SPACE BASE FORTY!

HELLO-HUER? BUCK CALLING! YOUR "GERRYSCOPE" WORKED! "INVISIBLE" MARTIAN SHIPS SHOWED UP PLAIN AS DAY! WE WIPED THEM OUT! NO LOSSES!

THAT'S **GREAT**, BUCK! BUT NOW RETURN TO EARTH! HAVE STARTLING **NEWS!**

AND **HURRY!**

BUCK! SO YOUR ROCKET RANGERS BEAT OFF THE MARTIAN ATTACK! GREAT! BUT I'VE A BETTER-AND **SAFER** WAY OF GETTING LEASE-LEND SUPPLIES TO **JUPITER!**

YOU HAVE? **HOW?**

MY BOY, I'VE DISCOVERED THE FORMULA OF THAT MAGIC MARTIAN POWDER MAJOR KNOTT USED! AND-I'VE **IMPROVED** ON IT?

THE POWDER REDUCES ANY OBJECT TO ATOMS! WITH THIS CANNON I CAN SEND THE ATOMS WHEREVER I WISH!

AND WHEN THEY REACH THE DESIRED POINT, THE ATOMS RE-ASSEMBLE INTO THEIR ORIGINAL FORM?

EXACTLY! GET UP ON THE TABLE! STAND DIRECTLY IN FRONT OF THE CANNON!

SAY! I DON'T WANT TO GO ANYWHERE

THIS EXPERIMENT IS IN THE INTEREST OF SCIENCE! IT **MAY-WIN-THE-WAR- FOR EARTH!**

OKAY, HUER! IF IT'LL LICK MADWOLF HETLAH, I'M YOUR GUINEA PIG!

HEH! THERE GOES A **SOLDIER!** BUT THIS TIME BUCK'S A SOLDIER OF **SCIENCE!**

I TOOK EVERY PRECAUTION! BUCK HAS BEEN REDUCED TO ATOMS! NOW-HEH! IF HE ONLY COMES TOGETHER AGAIN-AT THE **RIGHT SPOT!**

IF HE DOESN'T, I'LL NEVER FORGIVE MYSELF!

BUCK ROGERS ROCKET RANGERS IS AN ORGANIZATION OF **BOYS** AND **GIRLS** THE WORLD OVER, DEDICATED TO FREEDOM AND DEMOCRACY· WE STAND FOR LOYALTY TO OUR COUNTRY AND OUR FLAG! WE PLEDGE TRUTH AND HONESTY OF PURPOSE IN ALL THINGS. **WE ARE ROCKET RANGERS.** JOIN US!

WRITE BUCK ROGERS C/O THIS PAPER, ENCLOSE STAMPED (3¢) SELF-ADDRESSED ENVELOPE!

IN MY QUARTERS -SEVEN MILES FROM HUER'S LABORATORY!

WELL! I'LL BE **ROCKET BLASTED!** HERE I AM- IN MY **OWN ROOM!** AND I DON'T REMEMBER **GETTING HERE!**

HEH! BUCK! THIS IS HUER! CAN YOU **HEAR ME?**

ARE YOU **THERE,** BUCK? DID THE ATOM SMASHER WORK ALL RIGHT?

MARVELOUS, DOCTOR! YOU JUDGED IT TO THE FRACTION OF AN **INCH!**

BUCK ROGERS IN THE 25th CENTURY

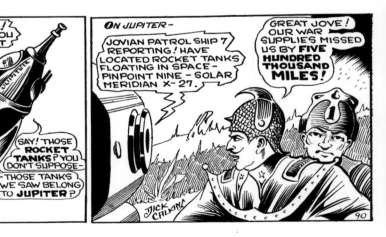

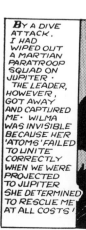

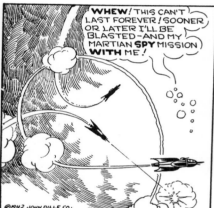

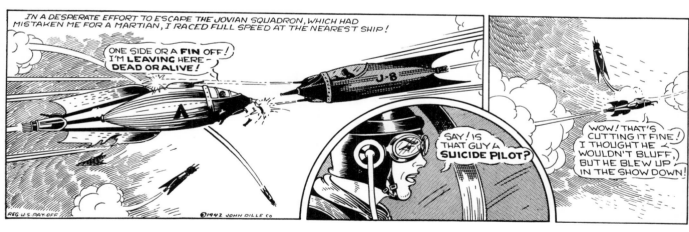

MARTIANS INVADE JUPITER

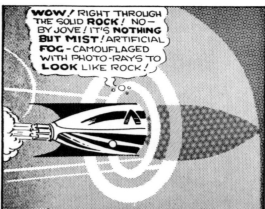

MARTIANS INVADE JUPITER

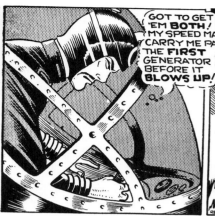

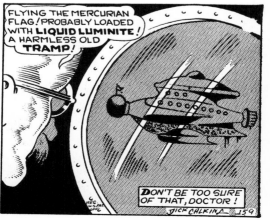

WHEN WILMA REACHED HUER'S POSITION——.
THE MARTIANS MUST HAVE DESTROYED HUER'S TRANSPORT. ONLY **ONE** SPACE-BELL ESCAPED! WHO'S **IN** IT? I'M AFRAID TO **LOOK!**

IT'S TOO MUCH TO HOPE THAT HUER COULD BE THE ONLY SURVIVOR! BUT IF HE **ISN'T** - SOLAR SCIENCE WILL **COLLAPSE!**

BLESS MY SPECS! AM I **SPACE-DAFFY** - OR IS THAT ONE OF OUR **ROCKET RANGERS** FLOATING TOWARD ME?

DOCTOR HUER! IT **IS** YOU! YOU'RE ALL RIGHT? TELL ME YOU'RE **SAFE!**

HEH! A SPACE HELMET! AND NO **HEAD** IN IT! YET - IT **SPEAKS!**

DON'T BE ALARMED DOCTOR HUER! THIS SPACE HELMET ISN'T **EMPTY!** I'M JUST **INVISIBLE!** DON'T YOU - RECOGNIZE ME?

WILMA DEERING! BLESS MY SPECS!

I CAN'T TAKE YOU ABOARD MY SHIP, DOCTOR! YOU HAVE NO SPACE SUIT TO GET THERE WITH .

HEH! HOW WILL I REACH **JUPITER?**

ON THE **TAIL** OF MY KITE, DOCTOR!

HEH! A **SPACE TRAILER!** I NEVER THOUGHT I'D COME TO **THIS!**

ON A NEARBY ASTEROID WAS A MARTIAN SPACECRAFT OBSERVATION POST!

ARMY FLASH! POST 6! JOVIAN FIGHTING SHIP, TOWING METAL BALL POSITION X-Z 754! PROBABLY LAYING A **SPACE MINE!** ATTENTION - PATROL!

DESTROY THAT JOVIAN SHIP! BUT DON'T HIT THE METAL BALL! OUR HIGH COMMAND WILL WANT TO EXAMINE IT!

IT MAY BE FULL OF **PRICELESS GEMS!**

NO DOUBT THE JOVIAN TREASURY IS MOVING ITS **TREASURE,** KNOWING WE MARTIANS WILL SOON BE **INVADING** JUPITER!

OR IT COULD BE A NEW TYPE OF SPACE **TORPEDO!**

INSIDE THE METAL LIFE-BELL —

BLESS MY SPECS! HOW THIS BALL DOES **ROLL AND TOSS!** I'M AFRAID **I'M** GOING TO BE — AH - **UPSET!**

I KNOW I AM!

HERE COMES ANOTHER MARTIAN **SPACEWOLF!**

THE FORCE OF THE EXPLOSION TORE THE BOMB CASING CONTAINING MAJOR GORDIAN KNOTT LOOSE FROM ITS RACK BENEATH MY SHIP!

THE SPACE TORPEDO, WITH ITS HUMAN CARGO, PLUNGED SWIFTLY TOWARD THE ROCKY SURFACE OF MARS!

IN MY SHIP —

MISSION - ACCOMPLISHED! I MUST GET AWAY - **FAST!** MARS - IS - **UNHEALTHY** SPOT - FOR A - **SPY!** I FEEL WEAK - THAT CONCUSSION -

SET - GYRO COMPASS - FOR **JUPITER!** HOPE - SHIP - HOLDS - TOGETHER! EVER'THING - GETTING - **DARK!**

BUY BATTLE BONDS

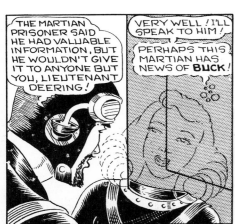

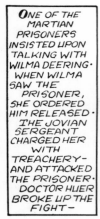

MARTIANS INVADE JUPITER

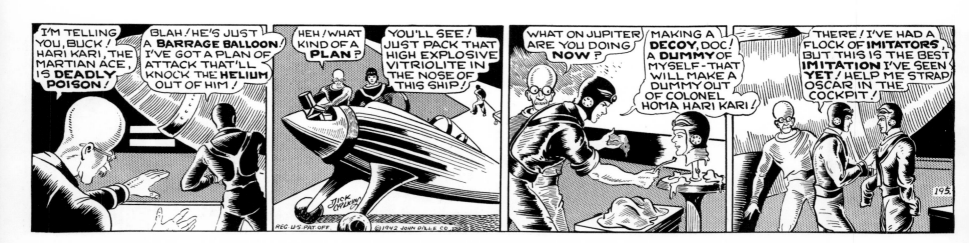

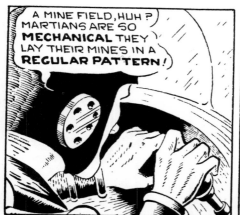

ACCORDING TO MY DETECTOR, I'M THROUGH THE MARTIAN SPACE MINE FIELD! ALL IN **ONE PIECE**! NOW I'LL SEND MY **DECOY** SHIP FAR AHEAD OF ME—

AND I'LL SCREEN MY **OWN** CRATE IN **ARTIFICIAL FOG**! HARI KARI WILL LEARN THAT **TWO** CAN PLAY **BLIND MAN'S BLUFF**!

©1942 JOHN DILLE CO

THERE! I'M JUST A HARMLESS LOOKING **CLOUD**! BUT HARI KARI, THE MARTIAN ACE, WILL FIND ME **LOADED WITH STORMY WEATHER**!

AND—LATER—A MARTIAN OBSERVER SAW **THIS** SET-UP IN HIS TELEVIEW·

PX-47

A PX-47! **BUCK ROGERS'** SHIP! COMING INTO OUR **CLAWS**!

REG.U.S.PAT.OFF

200

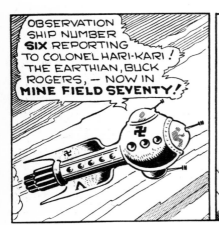

OBSERVATION SHIP NUMBER **SIX** REPORTING TO COLONEL HARI-KARI! THE EARTHIAN, BUCK ROGERS,—NOW IN **MINE FIELD SEVENTY**!

COLONEL KARI TALKING! CUT POWER ON FIELD SPACE MINES!—DON'T WANT ROGERS BLOWN UP!—WANT TO WRECK HIM **MYSELF**!

AH! LIEUTENANT TOGO! ORDER MY FIGHTER SQUADRONS TO STATIONS! I ARE GOING INTO USUAL **SINGLE COMBAT**!

AND, TOGO, SEE TO HER THAT ROGERS IS **BOXED IN**! THEN **ME** WILL DEAL HIM THE **DEATH BLOW**!

WILL DO, PLEASE!

201

COLONEL HARI KARI, THE MARTIAN ACE, WAS INFORMED THAT MY PX-47 DECOY SHIP HAD COME WITHIN STRIKING DISTANCE! THINKING I WAS IN HER, HE DIVED TO THE ATTACK!

FROM MY "CLOUD CAMOUFLAGE"—

AH! HERE COMES THE GREAT **HARI-KARI**—FOR SINGLE COMBAT! BUT HIS IDEA OF **SINGLE** SEEMS TO **PLURAL**!

CRIPPLE THAT SHIP! THEN I'LL CLOSE IN FOR THE **MERCY SHOT**! HARI KARI SIGNING OFF!

PX-47

©1942 JOHN DILLE CO

THOSE YELLOW RATS DON'T DARE FIGHT ON **EVEN** TERMS! THEY WANT ODDS OF **TEN TO ONE** BEFORE THEY BARE THEIR **BUCK TEETH**!

REG.U.S. PAT.OFF.

202

COLONEL HARI KARI, THE MARTIAN ACE—WITH HIS GANG OF FLYING CUTTHROATS DIVED ON MY DECOY SHIP· I WAS HIDDEN IN ARTIFICIAL FOG UNSEEN BY THE ENEMY PILOTS!

NOW **FOR** IT! I'LL JIGGLE THESE REMOTE CONTROL DIALS, AND MY **DECOY** SHIP WILL STAGGER AS THOUGH **BADLY HIT**! THEN—

COLONEL HARI KARI FELL NEATLY INTO MY BAITED TRAP—

CEASE FIRING! BUCK ROGERS' SHIP IS **CRIPPLED**! HE'S TRYING TO ESCAPE—THE COWARD—**AFTER HIM, MEN! HEAD HIM OFF**!

THERE THEY **GO**—AFTER MY **DECOY**! AND **HERE I GO**—AFTER **THEM**!

©1942 JOHN DILLE CO

REG.U.S. PAT.OFF

203

I SHOULD HAVE **KNOWN** BETTER THAN TO TRUST THAT SLANT-EYED HYENA! HE USED THAT **FIRE** GAG AS A **SCREEN**-TO CATCH ME OFF **GUARD!**

HIS SO-CALLED FIRE IS NOTHING BUT A **SMOKE BOMB**-RELEASED FROM INSIDE HIS SHIP, TO GIVE THE EFFECT OF BURNING ROCKET FUEL!

IF **THAT'S** THE WAY YOU SURRENDER, HARI KARI, I'LL GIVE YOU A SLICE OF **PEACE PIE**! CHEW **THAT** UP AND SWALLOW IT!

WOW! THERE GOES MY **TOP TURRET!** THE RAT'S FIGHTING **BACK**-FOR THE FIRST TIME IN HIS LIFE, I'LL BET! **GOOD!** THIS BEGINS TO LOOK **INTERESTING!**

208

TRUE TO HIS TREACHEROUS BREED, HARI KARI PRE-TENDED TO SURRENDER AS I WAS FORCING HIM INTO SINGLE COMBAT. THEN HE TURNED LIKE A CORNERED RAT AND STRUCK!

TOP GUN GONE! BUT MY OTHER TWO FORWARD WARDOGS CAN STILL BARK! AND **BITE**-I HOPE!

HARI KARI'S CRATE HAS PLENTY OF SOUP-BUT HE MUSHES ON HIS TURNS! HE'S A LOUSY PILOT! I CAN FLY A TIGHTER CIRCLE! HE'S IN FOR **TROUBLE!**

HE'S COMING INTO MY RINGSIGHT LIKE A CHICKEN SNAKE IN A HENHOUSE! WHAT A BEAUTIFUL SIGHT! I FEEL—

-LIKE AN ANCIENT **SUB** COMMANDER WITH A JAP AIRCRAFT CARRIER IN HIS PERISCOPE! OH BOY! HERE'S **SHOOTIN'** AT YOU, HARI KARI!

209

PEEPING JEEPS! MY **GUNS!** THEY'RE SHOOTING AROUND **CORNERS!** HARI KARI'S UNLUCKY SHOT MUST HAVE UPSET THE DELICATE **RAY** PROJECTORS!

SON OF THE **SUN!** WHAT SORT OF NEW **SECRET WEAPON** IS ROGERS **USING?** HIS BLASTED GUNS THROW **CURVES!**

WHOOSH!!

I'M GETTING OUT OF HERE!

I'M GETTING OUT OF HERE!

OH **NO**, YOU'RE NOT, HARI KARI! I **HEARD** THAT CRACK! YOU'RE ON THE **AIR!** SO— **I COMING FOR YOU!**

210

HARI KARI GOT OUT OF MY **TRAP!** BUT I'LL STAY ON HIS TAIL 'TIL THE **SUN** FREEZES OVER!

BLAST ROGERS! HE'S **GAINING** ON ME! **HAI!** A **METEORITE** AHEAD! MAYBE— PERHAPS—WE'LL **SEE!**

'ROUND AND 'ROUND THE BARB'RY BUSH THE MONKEY CHASED THE WEASEL! THIS'LL MAKE A **MONKEY** OUT OF ROGERS!

SAY! THAT MARTIAN'S **CLEVER!** I CAN'T CUT **INSIDE** OF HIM FOR A SHOT WITHOUT HITTING THAT **METEORITE!** WHY, THIS COULD GO ON UNTIL ONE OF US RUNS OUT OF **FUEL!**

211

MARTIANS INVADE JUPITER

MARTIANS INVADE JUPITER

MARTIANS INVADE JUPITER

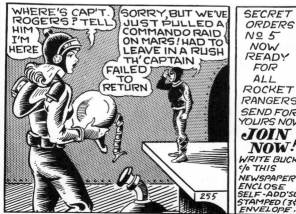

10
THE MONKEYMEN OF PLANET X

THE MONKEYMEN OF PLANET X

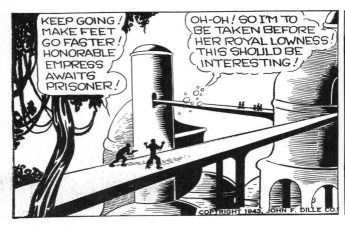

THE MONKEYMEN OF PLANET X

THE MONKEYMEN OF PLANET X

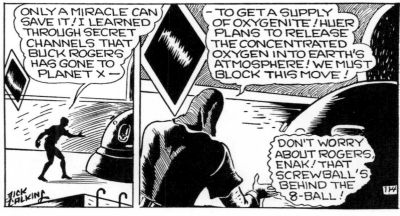

11
THE ATOMITES

THE ATOMITES

THE ATOMITES

x

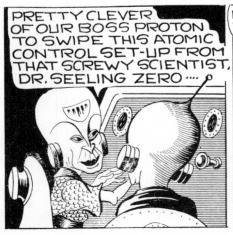

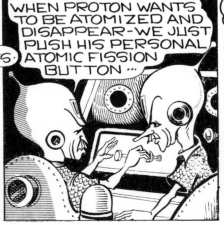

THE ATOMITES

THE ATOMITES

THE ATOMITES

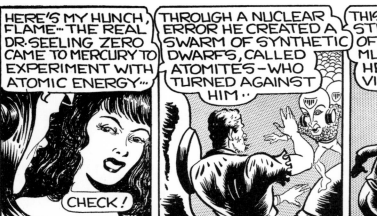

HERE'S MY HUNCH, FLAME... THE REAL DR. SEELING ZERO CAME TO MERCURY TO EXPERIMENT WITH ATOMIC ENERGY...

CHECK!

THROUGH A NUCLEAR ERROR HE CREATED A SWARM OF SYNTHETIC DWARFS, CALLED ATOMITES—WHO TURNED AGAINST HIM..

THIS NOVA KANE CHARACTER STEPPED IN, GOT CONTROL OF THE ATOMITES, AND MURDERED DR. ZERO. HE THEN TOOK HIS VICTIM'S IDENTITY!

Z-ZAP

©1946 JOHN DILLE CO. REG. U.S. PAT. OFF.

NOVA KANE PLANS TO DESTROY THE SOLAR SYSTEM—AND EARTH!

HIS DRONE BOMBERS ARE BLASTING THE MILKY WAY **RIGHT NOW!**

MEANTIME, A GAUNT AND EMACIATED SCARECROW STAGGERS ACROSS A VAST SEA OF ROCK AND SAND!

10/19

NO LUCK, FLAME.. I CAN'T FIND THE ATOMIC CONTROL SWITCH TO SHUT OFF THE POWER!

NOVA'S DRONE BOMBERS WILL DESTROY THE UNIVERSE, UNLESS—

THE MASTER SWITCH MIGHT BE IN HERE...

NOPE.. JUST AN EMPTY ROOM! GOT TO TRY ANOTHER ANGLE... COME ON, FLAME—

HEY! WHERE'S THE **DOOR** WE JUST CAME THROUGH?

WHY—IT'S GONE! NOTHING BUT SOLID WALLS—ALL AROUND US!

©1946 JOHN DILLE CO. REGUS PAT OFF.

NO DOOR? IMPOSSIBLE! WE ENTERED THIS ROOM THROUGH A **DOOR**-JUST A MINUTE AGO!

AND NOW THERE ISN'T EVEN A CRACK WHERE A DOOR COULD HAVE BEEN!

©1946 JOHN DILLE CO. REGUSPATOFF.

BUCK! WE'RE **TRAPPED!** SEALED UP **ALIVE!** WE'LL **SUFFOCATE!**

KEEP YOUR FLAPS DOWN, FLAME! DON'T LOSE YOUR HEAD! WE **KNOW** THERE'S A DOOR HERE...

KILROY WAS HERE

AND WE'LL FIND IT, TOO! YOU GO LEFT—I'LL GO RIGHT... FEEL EVERY INCH OF WALL SPACE!

OKAY, BUCK, BUT I'M AFRAID IT'S NO USE!

MEANTIME, A MYSTERIOUS FIGURE MAKES ITS WEARY WAY ACROSS A BLEAK AND DESOLATE PLAIN... 10-22

FOUND ANY SIGN OF THAT HIDDEN DOOR, FLAME?

NOTHING BUT SMOOTH WALLS—WALLS THAT SEAL US IN THIS DEATH-TRAP!

HAVING A LITTLE DIFFICULTY, ROGERS?

IT'S **NOVA KANE**- TALKING THROUGH THE WALL-COME TO MOCK US IN OUR LAST HOUR!

REGUSPATOFF

YES, FLAME, IT'S NOVA KANE! BUT I'M NOT TALKING THROUGH THE WALL, BABE!

I'M RIGHT HERE IN THE ROOM WITH YOU TWO CHARMING PEOPLE...HA-HA-**HA!**

KILROY WAS HERE

©1946 JOHN DILLE CO. 10-23

HOWDY, EARTHFOLKS!
BEST REGARDS
BUCK
ROGERS

COMPLIMENTS OF
PHIL NOWLAN
AND
DICK
CALKINS

**OTHER WORLDS
OF BUCK ROGERS**

form of orders or options based on current exchange prices of securiti
or commodities, but without any actual buying or selling of the prop
erty.

buck'eye' (bŭk'ī'), n. [*buck* animal + *eye*.] — from the appearance
of the seed.] 1. Any of several shrubs and trees of the same genus
(*Aesculus*) as the horse chestnut, esp. *A. glabra*. 2. [*cap.*] Colloq.,
U. S. A native of Ohio, the **Buckeye State**; — a nickname.
buck fever. Colloq., U. S. Excitement at the sight of game, such as
often unnerves a novice in hunting.
buck'hound' (bŭk'hound'), n. The Scottish deerhound.
buck'ish, adj. Dandified; impetuous. — **buck'ish·ly**, adv.
buck'le (bŭk'l), n. [OF. *bocle*, *boucle*, boss of a shield, fr. L. *buccula*,
dim. of *bucca* cheek; this boss resembling a cheek.] 1. A fastening
for two loose ends, as of a belt or strap. 2. A similar device of orna-
mental design, as on women's shoes. 3. *Archaic.* A crisp curl of hair.
— v. t.; BUCK'LED (-'ld); BUCK'LING (-lĭng). 1. To fasten with a
buckle. 2. To apply (oneself) with vigor. — v. i. 1. To prepare
oneself for an undertaking, as, orig., by buckling on the armor; hence,
to apply oneself with vigor; — often with *to* or *down to*. 2. To struggle; grapple; contend.
buck'le, v. t. & i. To bend permanently; to become distorted; to
crumple up; as, the freight train *buckled* in the middle. — n. A dis-
tortion, as a bulge, bend, kink, or twist in a beam, a tube, etc.
buck'ler (bŭk'lẽr), n. [OF. *boucler* a shield with a boss, fr. *bocle*,
boucle, boss. See 1st BUCKLE.] 1. A kind of shield worn on one of
the arms to protect the front of the body. 2. Figuratively, one who
or that which protects or defends. — v. t. To shield or defend.
buck'o (bŭk'ō), n.; pl. BUCKOES (-ōz). A domineering, bullying fellow; a bully.
buck private. *Slang, U.S.* A private soldier, esp. a new recruit.
buck'ra (bŭk'rá), n. [In a Calabar coast dial. *mŏkara*, *mbŏkara*.]
A white man; master. — adj. White; white man's; strong; good.
Both Orig. Negro Dial.
buck'ram (bŭk'ram), n. [OF. *boquerant*, fr. Pers. ... Bokhara.]
1. Formerly, a fabric of fine linen or cotton for garm... A
coarse cloth of linen or hemp, stiffened with sizing. b A stiffe cloth
of cotton, used for binding books, for wrappers, etc. 3. Stiffe
precise formality. — adj. Made of buckram; hence, stiff; precise
— v. t. To strengthen with buckram; also, to make pretentious.

Buck Rog'ers (bŭk' rä' jẽrz), n. 1. the
original and most celebrated comic-strip
spaceman. 2. a space-sleuth and command-
ing officer of the Satellite Pioneers. adj. 1.
of Buck Rogers. 2. of or pertaining to all
things scientific. 3. of or pertaining to all
things futuristic: as, the coming *Buck
Rogers* era. 4. a synonym for top-notch
science-fiction adventure. 5. daring.

buck'saw' (bŭk'sô'), n. A saw set in a deep H-shaped frame, used ir
sawing wood on a sawbuck, or sawhorse. See SAW, *Illust.*
buck'shee (bŭk'shē'; bŭk'shē'), adj. [See BAKSHEESH.] Brit ...
Slang. Free of charge; gratis.
buck'shot' (bŭk'shŏt'), n. A coarse leaden shot for a game, between ... inch in diameter.
buck'skin (bŭk' ...). ... A strong soft
leather, usually yellow... cream-white, closely woven
woolen cloth (**buckskin cloth**). 4. *pl.* Breeches made of buckskin.
b A person clothed in buckskin, esp. [*cap.*] an American soldier of the
Revolutionary War. a *Western U.S.* A buckskin-colored horse. —
buck'skin', adj.
buck'tail' (-tāl'), n. *Angling.* An artificial fly made of hairs from the
tail of a deer, or similar material. See LURE, *Illust.*
buck'thorn' (-thôrn'), n. 1. Any of a genus (*Rhamnus*, type of the
family Rhamnaceae, the buckthorn family) of trees or shrubs, some of
which have thorny branches; as, the *cascara* buckthorn (see CASCARA
1). 2. A tree (*Bumelia lycioides*) of the southern United States, of
the sapotilla family.
buck'tooth' (-tōōth'), n. Any tooth that juts out.
buck'wheat' (-hwēt'), n. [*Buck* beech tree + *wheat*.] 1. An herb
of the genus *Fagopyrum* typifying a family (Polygonaceae, the buckwheat family) characterized by mostly entire leaves with stipules form-
ing a sheath around the stem, and apetalous flowers arranged in spikes.
It is cultivated as a food plant. 2. The triangular seed of this plant
ground into flour (**buckwheat flour**).
bu·col'ic (bū-kŏl'ĭk), adj. [L. *bucolicus*, fr. Gr. *boukolikos*, fr. *bou-
kolos* cowherd; herdsman.] Pastoral; rustic. — Syn. See RURAL.
— n. 1. A pastoral poem; an eclogue or idyl. 2. *Humorous.* A
rustic; a farmer. — **bu·col'i·cal** (-ĭ·kål), adj. — **bu·col'i·cal·ly**, adv.
bud (bŭd), n. [ME. *budde*.] 1. *Bot.* An undeveloped shoot or stem;
a small axillary or terminal protuberance on the stem of a plant, con-
sisting of rudimentary foliage or floral leaves. Cf. CION. 2. A person
or thing not yet mature. 3. *Bot. & Zool.* A protuberance of a part of
the body which develops into a new organism; a gemma.
— v. i.; BUD'DED; BUD'DING. To put forth buds; to develop, as a bud;
hence, to be like a bud in youth and freshness, or growth and promise.
— v. t. 1. To put forth as buds; to cause to bud. 2. *Hort.* To insert a bud of (a specified variety, etc.) into an opening in the bark of a
different stock, esp. for propagating desired varieties; as, to *bud* a rose.
Cf. GRAFT, v. t. 1. — **bud'der**, n.
Bud'dha (bōō'l'ä), n. [Skr. *buddha* awakened, enlightened.]
title of an incarnation of self-abnegation, virtue, and wisdom
form of a religious teacher of the Buddhists who ...
Gautama Siddhartha (563–483 B.C.), founder of ...
Bud'dhism (-ĭz'm), n. The religion of centra...
upon the doctrine of Gautama Buddha teac...
from liability to s... ...

L.
budu
budg'
bud seal.
external ...
of hair, g
bud sport.
bud variati
the develop.
bud, as a ...
tion involving ...
buff (bŭf), n. [F
A superior leather
elk, etc. 2. A m
skin; as, to strip to
of medium saturati
wood covered with
buffing wheel. — a
buff. — v. t. 1. To
like. 2. To give a buff
stain buff.
buff, n. [OF. *buffe*. See
Dial., exc. in "blindman's
buf'fa·lo (bŭf'á-lō), n.; pl.
buffalo, bufalo, fr. L. *bufa*
zelle, also the buffalo or wil
Any of several species of w.
bubalus) of India, now dome
Asia and adjacent islands, th
Africa, and the American bison
skin. b A buffalo fish. — v. t.
overawe; as, to get one *buffalo*ed.
buffalo berry. a The edible scarl
(*Shepherdia argentea*) and S. canade
astern United States, having sil
...; — called also **buffalo bush**
buffalo bug. — CARPET BEETLE.
buffalo ... Any of several large fi
chiefly the Mississippi Valley.
buffalo grass. A low-growing grass (.
mon on former feeding grounds of th
States.
buffalo moth. The larva of the carpet l
buff'er (bŭf'ẽr), n. [From BUFF to deade
blow.] Anything, such as a fender or bu
shock or bear the brunt of a collision.
buff'er, n. A worker or machine that h
specif., a polisher, as for fingernails.
buffer state. A small independent stat
usually rival, states.
buf'fet (bŭf'ĕt; -ĭt), n. [OF., a slap ir
blow, as with the hand; a slap. — v
strike repeatedly; also, to strive with
To strike; contend. 2. To make or
— **buf'fet·er**, n.
buf·fet' (bōō-fā'; bŭ-fā'; b↵·fā'; Brit
bōōf'ā' for sense 3), n. [F.] 1. ...
3. A cupboard or set of shelves
3. A counter for refreshments, :
bū-fā'; bōō-fā'; *see the noun*), a
at a table; hence, without formi
buff'ing wheel (bŭf'ĭng). Mac
muslin, or the like, and used in
buf'fle·head' (bŭf'l·hĕd'), n. [
small North American duck (
goldeneye.
||**buf'fo** (bōōf'fō), n. *masc.; pl*
comic roles in opera, often a b
buf·foon' (bŭ-fōōn'; bŭ-), n
who makes a business of a ...
etc.; a clown. — **Syn.** ...
— **buf·foon'ish**, adj.
bug (bŭg), n. [ME
boozy. 2. a U.S.
most any kind, esp
beetle; as, the po
ism, esp. one t
paratus or in
bug'a·boo'
nary or ...
bug... ...

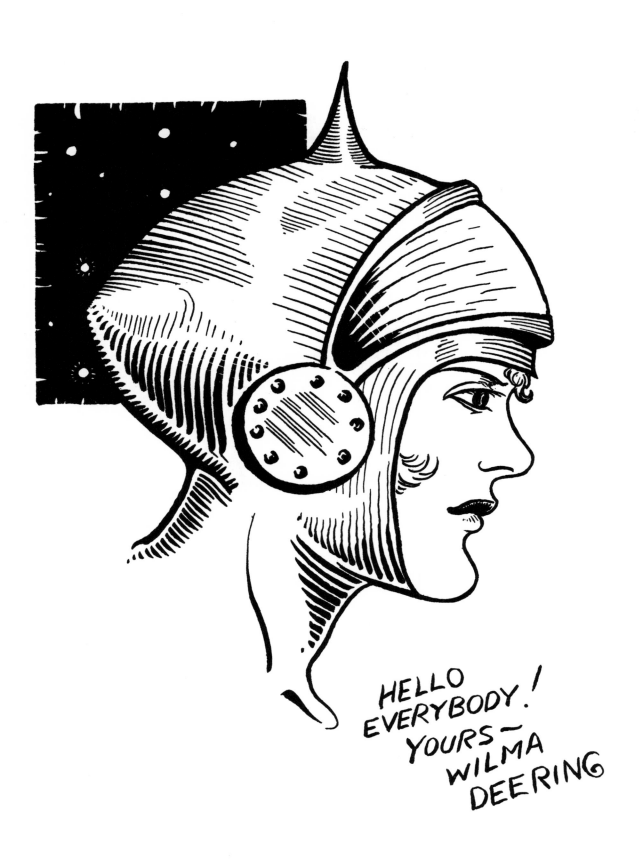

CHARACTERS

BUCK ROGERS— A clean-cut, athletic, adventurous 20th-Century youth. His voice is clear, pleasant and good-humored. He speaks in a straightforward, unaffected way; vigorous, alert, and for the most part commandingly. He is a 20th-Century lad who accidentally was thrown into a state of suspended animation, to wake up in the 25th-Century and find a world of scientific marvels, which, however, do not overawe him. With the adaptability of youth, and self reliance, he fits himself into the picture of the 25th Century and the opportunities for amazing adventure that it offers.

WILMA DEERING—The feminine counterpart of Buck; a soldier-girl of the 25th-Century, boyish, sweet, courageous and loyal, she is Buck's capable companion in these amazing adventures. She hasn't quite Buck's decisiveness and determination, but a will and opinions of her own. She is not self-conscious. Her voice should reveal no affectation; should be pleasant, enthusiastic.

BYRON—A veteran space navigator, middle-aged, hearty and hale. Suggest a heavy voice, or at least one that contrasts with Buck's.

FIRST, SECOND and THIRD VOICES—Those of sub-officers on the space ship, one of whom might be a girl. In this episode the tinny quality of the "loudspeaker" will alter them somewhat. They might be the same actors who, in following installments, take parts of KILLER KANE and ARDALA, and possibly BUCK or BYRON could double for one of them.

NOTE: KILLER KANE (in following installments) is a vigorous, virile, snarling, mean, hateful type of villain without a redeeming feature; utterly consciousless, shrewd, alert, forceful, cruel, capable.

ARDALA—his feminine partner in crime, is a scheming, conscienceless, cruel vamp. Her only virtue or weakness is her loyalty to Kane, which is due to her inability to dominate or influence him. She is sly, purring and treacherous, a sleek tigress.

Actors should go as far as possible in portraying the meanness and villainy of these two characters without a comedy or caricature note.

Play and sing theme song chorus. Repeat, playing only, and fading out as announcer begins to speak after two or three bars.

ANNOUNCER—Tonight there comes to us the first of a series of BUCK ROGERS HOURS—of breathless, dramatic adventure IN THE FUTURE—FIVE HUNDRED YEARS from now —when Science shall have bridged the voids of space between EARTH and her SISTER PLANTS—And EARTHMEN, no longer tied to the surface of their relatively tiny world by the bonds of gravity, shall seek their destiny in the CONQUEST OF AN ENTIRE UNIVERSE! *(Slight pause)*

   These stirring episodes of adventure in the TWENTY FIFTH CENTURY come to us through the courtesy of   (Insert Advertiser's Message).

   BUCK ROGERS—as is well known to the MILLIONS of you who follow his adventures in his daily picture story, written by PHIL NOWLAN and drawn by DICK CALKINS for the LEADING NEWSPAPERS OF AMERI-CA—is the youth who fell asleep in 1932, spent FIVE HUNDRED YEARS in a state of SUSPENDED ANIMA-TION, and awoke in TWENTY-FOUR-THIRTY-TWO, A.D., with his YOUTH and VIGOR UNIMPAIRED—to find a world of SCIENTIFIC MARVELS!—And *(meaningly)* ALSO—to meet that LOYAL—COURAGEOUS—SELF-RELIANT girl of the Twenty-fifth Century—WILMA DEERING—who, with Buck, so well typifies the interests, ideals and hopes of American youth in the future—and who, with Buck, dared the dangers of INTER-PLANETARY SPACE in the FIRST explorations of EARTHMEN among OTHER worlds of the Solar System.

   TONIGHT we begin the broadcast of a HITHERTO UNPUBLISHED adventure of Buck and Wilma, which began shortly after Buck was made commander of the FIRST SHIP of the Interplanetary Rocket Patrol, known as the IRP, organized by the Governments of Earth for the protection of their pioneer commerce

with the Planet MARS. For CRIME, ever ready to turn the achievements of SCIENCE to its OWN ends, already had crept forth INTO THE VOIDS OF SPACE—to PREY upon the AMAZINGLY VALUABLE *(Fade in theme music)* commerce between the two planets—and to BOOTLEG the products of ONE world among the nations of the OTHER!

(Theme music swells for a bar or two then softens to faint background through following, as announcer resumes;)

So let us twirl the dials of our TELERADIOSCOPE—and tune in a scene—the main control cabin of the patrol ship—far out in space—BUCK and WILMA, trim and snappy in the scarlet, white and gold of the IRP, are at the great control board—with its MAZE of instruments, signals, and VISION LENSES! *(Fade out music. Fade in hissing sound that rises to a suppressed roar)*

ANNOUNCER, *raising voice, registering excitement and tension:* That ROAR we hear—It's the mighty blast of the ROCKET MOTORS!!—Out!—OUT!—Faster!—FASTER!!—FAR OUT INTO SPACE they are driving—AT EVER ACCELERATING SPEED!—For out here in empty space there is NO SUCH THING as AIR friction—or WEIGHT—to be overcome!—Buck flips a switch!—In the lens before him appears the face of the ASTRONAVIGATION OFFICER—and THEN—

(Announcer ceases—Roar grows louder for an instant—then fades to as-before)

BUCK, *crisp, authoritative voice*—Got your bearings, Byron?
BYRON, *his voice slightly tinny from loudspeaker*—Aye AYE, Captain Rogers—Straight as a hairline, sir!
BUCK—Any SIDE DRIFT?
BYRON—PRACTICALLY none, sir—Less than a MILLIONTH degree!
BUCK—Gravitational disturbance?
BYRON—None, sir—Just the normal pull from Earth and Venus in this POSITION!
BUCK—And what's our speed now, Byron?
BYRON—Eighty-thousand miles an hour, sir.
BUCK—Very good, Mr. Byron—Cut ALL rockets—We'll COAST to our station at this speed, without any further acceleration—I don't want any luminous trail of rocket-gas spreading out behind us.
BYRON, *snappily*—Aye aye, sir! *(then faintly in drawn-out shout)* ALL ROCKETS CUT!! *(Roaring fades out, ending with click as Buck snaps switch)*
BUCK, *audibly yawning*—Whooie!—WHAT a relief!—That rocket blast has been MASSAGING our ears for TEN SOLID HOURS, Wilma—ever since we roared away from Base, at Niagara.
WILMA, *pertly*—Is THAT why you cut the rockets?—To save your EARDRUMS?
BUCK, *a little disgustedly*—You KNOW it isn't—But we're going to spread NO COMET-TAIL OF IONIZED GAS from our exhaust to warn the SPACE PIRATES of our coming THIS time!
WILMA, *doubtfully*—I know—But we lose SO much time drifting along this way at constant speed—We'd reach our station MUCH quicker if we ACCELERATED for half the distance, and then DECELERATED for the OTHER half at the SAME RATE. *(Then, with mild petulance)*BESIDES, if we kept on accelerating the LIFT of the ship UNDER us would give us WEIGHT, and we could be COMFORTABLE!—I think it's DUMB to be drifting along this way WITHOUT any weight—to have to strap ourselves down, or go FLOATING HELPLESSLY around the cabin—BUCK, *interrupting, a bit irritably*—And so I suppose YOU'D like spread out a nice, big, glowing, expanding trail of IONIZED EXHAUST GASES that the PIRATES could see for TEN MILLION MILES—HUH?
WILMA, *apologetically*—Now don't be SILLY, Buck—You know I—what I mean—

(Trill of electric bell—click of switch—with faint hum as of an electric current, through following dialogue)

BYRON, *voice tinny as before*—Astronavigation Officer reporting, sir.
BUCK—Yes Byron—What is it?
BYRON—Gravity Disturbance-finders indicate a small object dead ahead, sir—Probably not more than eight tons mass—About ten or twelve thousand miles distant, sir—I can't get it any more definitely than THAT sir—as YET—owing to the extremely small mass.
WILMA, *quickly, with excitement*—It can't be a SPACE SHIP then!
BUCK—All right, Byron—Check it carefully, and report back, will you, as soon as you have its position accurately.—Probably only a METEOR—But we don't want to HIT it!
BYRON—I'll have the EXACT position for you in just a few minutes, sir.
(Faint hum ceases with a click)

WILMA, *thoughtfully*—Do you know, Buck—I've been THINKING.

BUCK, *with good-humored sarcasm*—GOOD!—What ABOUT?

WILMA, *still thoughtfully*—About—Well, about KILLER KANE.

BUCK, *indignantly*—Oh YEAH?—Well LISTEN, Sister—It's YOUR privelege to think sweet thoughts about ANY TWISTED SIZZLER you WANT to—when you're AGROUND—off DUTY!—But while you're second-officering THIS sky-wagon, you'll please keep your MIND—IF any—on your JOB!

WILMA, *freezingly*—With the Captain's PERMISSION—That was ENTIRELY uncalled for! As the Second-Officer was about to remark when the Skipper INTERRUPTED her—I was only going to say that NOTHING has been heard of KILLER KANE—or his girl-friend, Ardala—since their release from prison—and to ask if it has EVER occurred to you that—

BUCK, *suddenly interested and eager*—You MEAN?—That KILLER KANE—may have—

WILMA, *forgetting to be frigid*—May have originated this SPACE PIRACY RACKET?—EXACTLY! *(Then eagerly)* You KNOW, Buck, it wasn't a MONTH after they got out that they apparently VANISHED from the face of the Earth—And that was before—

BUCK, *excitedly*—Before the first transport was captured!—SIZZLING ROCKETS!!—I believe you've HIT on something, Wilma!—It SOUNDS like his work, all right—The RUTHLESS CRUELTY of it!—Opening the AIR VALVES!—The air in the ship HISSING OUT INTO SPACE—Men—women—children—gasping—fighting DESPERATELY for BREATH!—All the HEAT going out with the DISSIPATING AIR!—And THEN—And THEN, the TERRIBLE cold of OUTER SPACE!—and—and—

WILMA, *with a shuddering little moan*—Oh—Oh BUCK!—It must have been T-TERRIBLE!—I c-can't bear to ever THINK of it!!

BUCK, *a bit vindictively*—Well, I wouldn't put it PAST him!—He's THAT KIND!—Though Heaven knows it took YOU long enough to find it OUT.

WILMA, *embarrased*—Now Buck!—Why bring THAT up? You know it all happened LONG before he went RACKETEER, and there was NEVER anything really SERIOUS between us. And besides—

BUCK, *challengingly*—Besides WHAT?

WILMA, *demurely*—I didn't know YOU then.

BUCK, *weakly*—Oh!

WILMA, *sweetly*—You see, you were still ASLEEP then—I SOMETIMES think you never HAVE waked up to—to EVERYTHING. *(Then more hurriedly to cover her confusion)* But Killer Kane must have a base somewhere. It's surely not on EARTH or the International Police would have found it.

BUCK, *feeling on firmer ground now*—It must be on MARS, Wilma. He could get plenty of protection THERE from one or another of the rulers, simply by giving them a cut-in on the loot. The Martian Confederation has never been anything but an empty gesture, forced on the War Lords by their appetite for the luxuries of EARTH, and the terms of trade between the two planets. On the surface the War Lords are friendly, but SECRETLY they're ALL at one another's throats. The Martian nobility make no secret of their feuds, and the common people don't CARE, so long as THEY'RE not involved. You see how easily Kane could arrange it, by making a secret deal with one powerful ruler, who would protect him and make no report at all to the Confederation or the Joint Tax Board.

WILMA—Then why don't we just land on MARS and go straight AFTER him?

BUCK—NO-THING DO-ING!—It would take a YEAR to search that planet—And the hand of EVERY Martian would be against us, in SPITE of their pretended friendship. No no—

(Trill of electric bell interrupts him)

BUCK—Here's Byron reporting again—about that meteor, I imagine.

(Click of switch, and faint hum of communicator through conversation with Byron)

BYRON, *voice tinny as before, excited*—Astronavigation Officer reporting sir!—I have accurate bearings on—

BUCK—That meteor you reported a while ago? Good!—What do you make of it, Byron?

BYRON, *tense and excited*—A little over nine tons mass, sir!—Only FIVE THOUSAND miles off!—And DEAD AHEAD!—We're going to SMACK SQUARE INTO IT unless—

WILMA, *excited and frightened*—Unless we CHANGE OUR COURSE!—But how CAN we at THIS TERRIFIC SPEED?—It might mean DEATH!

BUCK, *tense and decisive*—We've got to RISK it!—Even if we only swing a quarter mile to one side, it ought to be enough!—Stand by your SIDE-BLASTS, Byron—Set 'em for minimum impulse—automatic cut-off!—We'll only need a SPLIT SECOND of it, but it may knock us ALL UNCONSCIOUS!—Wilma, throw the

alarm switch!

(A loud click) Cut in our microphone for ship-wide orders!—
(Clang of alarm gong, distant shouts and clamor)
(Buck adopts tone of train announcer, but speaking clearly)

EMERGENCY STA-TIONS!!!—AL-L HANDS STAND BY FOR CHANGE OF COURSE!—EVERY MAN IN SAFETY STRAPS! A R E Y O U R E A D Y? REPORT BY STATIONS! *(Aside rapidly)* Quick, Wilma!—Up against the wall!—The side-pressure's going to be terrific!

(Suppressed and distant turmoil continues, and above it a succession of different voices, metallic through loudspeaker, shouting distantly)

FIRST VOICE—Gun Crew—O-KA-A-AY!
SECOND VOICE—Gen-e-ra-tor Room—O-KA-A-AY!
THIRD VOICE—Rock-et Crew—O-KA-A-AY!
BYRON—Navigation Crew O-KA-A-AY!—Side blasts R E A D Y!
BUCK—F I R E SIDE BLASTS!—R-R-R-E-A-D-D-E-E-E!—*HEP!*

(Distant gong clangs—Distant shouts—a hissing roar starts—heavy objects bang against metal wall)

WILMA, *shrieks as rocket hisses, and*—Oh! OH! *OH!*—This PRESSURE!—OHHHH! *(Her scream ceases suddenly)*
BUCK—*Groans.*

(END ALL SOUND EFFECTS—DEAD SILENCE FOR AN INSTANT)

ANNOUNCER, *in quiet, conversational tone*—The strain of forcing that ship out of its course, even slightly, when going at the speed of EIGHTY THOUSAND MILES AN HOUR, must have been TERRIFIC!—WHAT, we wonder, was the effect of it?—Were the massive generators torn from their beds and hurled against the side walls?—Was the hull of the patrol ship strained or warped?—Were Buck and Wilma seriously injured when the terrific pressure flattened them against the metal wall of the control cabin?—And did the patrol ship manage to avoid collision with that nine-ton meteor?

These things will be revealed to us next   at this hour, when Buck Rogers and Wilma will continue their adventure in search of those pirates of space, Killer Kane and Ardala, through the courtesy of
(Advertiser's message)

During advertiser's message, toward close of it, theme music fades in and swells to full volume as announcer ceases. Voices come in on second chorus, and fade out all at expiration of time.

End of Installment 1, Episode 1.

BUCK ROGERS
MYSTERY COLOR PUZZLE

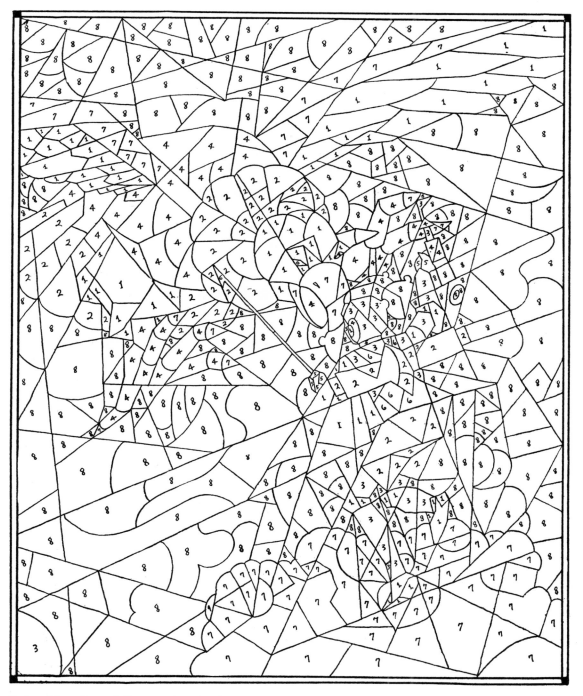

Color Numbered Spaces in the Picture Puzzle According to Key Numbers Indicated Below. Use either Water Colors or Crayons. To Obtain Best Results, Mount on Cardboard or Stiff Paper. A BIG SURPRISE AWAITS YOU! When Completed Hang on the Wall of Your Room.

RED	– – 1	ORANGE	– – 4	WHITE	– – 7
GREEN	– – 2	PINK	– – 5	BLUE	– – 8
YELLOW	– – 3	BLACK	– – 6		

BUCK ROGERS SOLAR SCOUTS

Earth Division

Official Enlistment Papers

Pursuant to orders from SCOUT PATROL UNIT, G. H. Q. NIAGARA, all applicants for enrollment in the BUCK ROGERS INTERPLANETARY SOLAR SCOUTS are requested to fill out this ENLISTMENT BLANK and return it to the headquarters immediately.

DATA REQUIRED

1. NAME ....
2. Age ....
3. Height ....
4. Weight ....
5. Color of Eyes ....
6. Color of Hair ....

7. School Grade ....
8. Favorite Sports ....
9. Previous Rocket Ship experience, if any........................
10. Favorite Newspaper Adventure Strip
....

BUCK ROGERS SOLAR SCOUTS must maintain passing grades in their school work to remain eligible for Interplanetary Duty! Those whose grades drop below the passing mark will be on their honor to correct such condition with all possible promptness. Remember - -

A GOOD SOLAR SCOUT GUIDES HIS OWN DESTINY TOWARD THE STARS!

I hereby apply for membership in BUCK ROGERS SOLAR SCOUTS, and promise to do my duty to God and Country. To be true to others and to myself. To be upright, honest, clean in mind and body, helpful to the weak and aged, and ever try to better myself in all ways, that I may be an asset to my PARENTS, my COUNTRY, the SOLAR SCOUTS, and myself.

Name .... Street .... City .... State ....

Mail this form to Buck Rogers Solar Scouts, in care of the paper in which you read Buck Rogers, enclosing self-addressed, stamped (3c) envelope in which you will receive your Official Identification Card with SECRET NUMBER.

By order of CAPTAIN BUCK ROGERS,
Commanding Officer - SOLAR SCOUTS - Earth Division

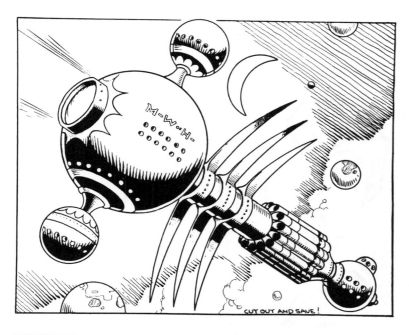

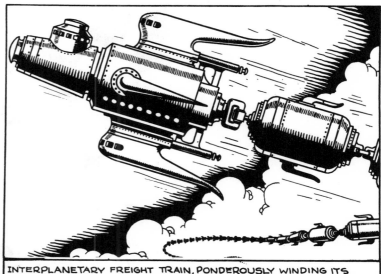

INTERPLANETARY FREIGHT TRAIN, PONDEROUSLY WINDING ITS SLUGGISH WAY THROUGH THE OUTER-SPACES AT 300 MILES PER MINUTE —— CAPABLE OF DRAWING 6500 "CARS"! CUT OUT AND SAVE!

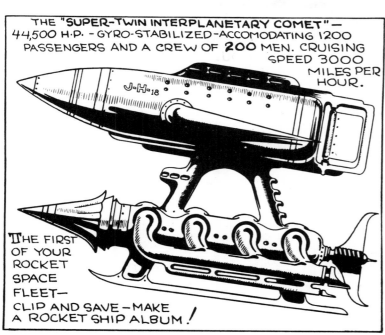

THE "SUPER-TWIN INTERPLANETARY COMET" — 44,500 H.P. - GYRO-STABILIZED - ACCOMODATING 1200 PASSENGERS AND A CREW OF **200** MEN. CRUISING SPEED 3000 MILES PER HOUR.

THE FIRST OF YOUR ROCKET SPACE FLEET — CLIP AND SAVE — MAKE A ROCKET SHIP ALBUM!

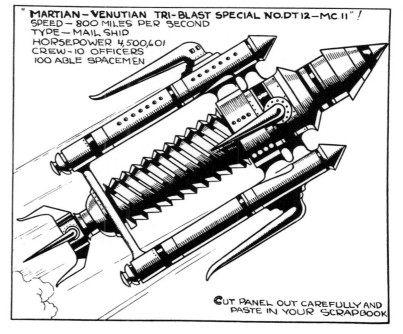

"MARTIAN - VENUTIAN TRI-BLAST SPECIAL NO. DT 12 — MC. 11"!
SPEED - 800 MILES PER SECOND
TYPE — MAIL SHIP
HORSEPOWER 4,500,601
CREW - 10 OFFICERS
100 ABLE SPACEMEN

CUT PANEL OUT CAREFULLY AND PASTE IN YOUR SCRAPBOOK

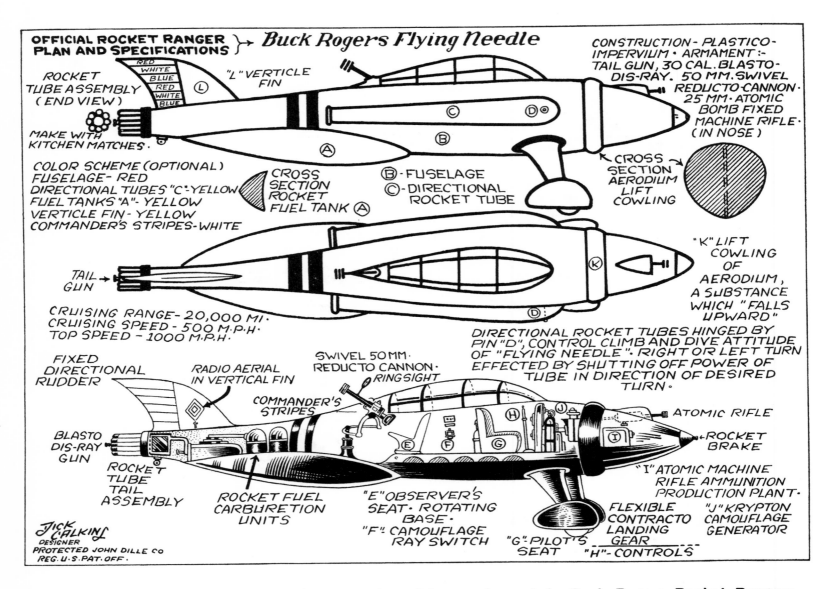

Read the Great Buck Rogers Strip every day. Advance in rank in Buck Rogers Rocket Rangers. Become a Space Ship Commander. Get your friends to join today.

The PLANET VENUS

AS IT UNFOLDED BEFORE THE ASTONISHED EYES OF BUDDY AND ALURA
FELLOW ADVENTURERS WITH—
BUCK ROGERS
BY PHIL NOWLAN & DICK CALKINS

UNEXPLORED

LAND OF THE DRAGON RIDERS

CAVE OF THE WINDS

GORRO'S CASTLE

LAND OF THE BIRD RIDERS

LAND OF MYSTERY ?

BUDDALURA

THE JUNGLE FOLK

SEA

BOILING EQUATORIAL

VERY HIGH MOUNTAINS

?

UNEXPLORED

UNEXPLORED

LAND OF THE GIANTS

AROMAKIA

Drawn by RUSS KEATON

POLAR ICE CAP

(A) Where the space ship first landed.
(B) Course sailed by the Aromak fleet, with which Buddy and Alura began their tour of the planet.
(C) Where Buddy and Alura were swept from the ship in storm.
(D) Crater, to which they flew on their flying belts, where Mercurian invaders had established themselves.

(E) Spot at which Buddy and Alura rejoined fleet after first battle with Mercurians.
(F) Aromakia—It was here that their rocket ship rejoined Buddy and Alura—and from here that they hopped off into space to fight the Mercurians.
(G) Scene of final battle with Mercurians.
(H) Cave of Winds, to which disabled rocket ship drifted after battle—Here Buddy and Alura

were carried underground, found the Little Folk, and led them forth to the surface.
(I) Gorro's Castle—where King Buddy was imprisoned, and from which he escaped with the aid of Queen Alura.
(J) Scene of the GREAT BATTLE, where Gorro was captured and the Rebels put to rout.
(K) Where Border Guard was attacked by strange machines.

© JOHN DILLE CO.

MOUNT ON CARDBOARD—COLOR WITH CRAYON OR WATER COLOR TO GET MOST STRIKING EFFECT.